ARTILLERY, MISSILES & MILITARY TRANSPORT

of the 20TH CENTURY

ARTILLERY, MISSILES & MILITARY TRANSPORT
of the 20TH CENTURY

Christopher Chant

Illustrated by John Batchelor

TIGER BOOKS INTERNATIONAL
LONDON

This edition published in 1996 by
Tiger Books International PLC, Twickenham
© Graham Beehag Books, Christchurch, Dorset
All rights reserved
Printed and bound in Singapore
ISBN 1-85501-806-3

Contents

General-Purpose Artillery

ARTILLERY is defined as a crew-served weapon firing a tube-launched projectile that was originally of the solid shot type, then the explosive-filled shell type, and can now be either of the shot or shell type depending on the purpose being served: the shot is used almost exclusively for the short-range destruction of hardened targets such as armoured fighting vehicles and strongpoints, while the shell (including its most recent cargo-carrying variant filled with submunitions) is used for virtually every other battlefield task.

The development of modern artillery began in the nineteenth century, when the well-established type of field and siege gun, loaded down its unrifled barrel first with black powder and then with its projectile (generally spherical although there were also cylindrical case and canister munitions), was gradually improved into a longer-ranged and more accurate weapon with a rifled barrel firing an elongated projectile that was loaded by means of an opening breech: this projectile was attached to the front of a brass case containing the propellant (originally black powder but then a nitrocellulose compound) to create a unitary round or, in the alternative separate-loading type of ammunition used for heavier guns, loaded in front of the one or more silk bags of propellant.

These developments did much to convert artillery from a short-ranged and relatively inaccurate type of weapon into a considerably longer-ranged and more accurate type that was standardised in two basic forms: as the gun and the howitzer. The gun is a direct-fire weapon used for the engagement of targets that are visible directly to the gunner, and fires at a higher muzzle velocity for a comparatively flat trajectory with the muzzle elevated to no more than 45 degrees. The howitzer, on the other hand, is an indirect-fire weapon used for the engagement of targets that are not directly visible to the gunner, and fires at a lower muzzle velocity for a high, lobbed trajectory with the muzzle elevated to more than 45 degrees. The gun is best suited to the destruction of shorter-range targets, while the howitzer is best suited to the engagement

Used in limited numbers during World War I, and most notably involved in the Japanese reduction of the German concession enclave at Tsingtao on the Chinese coast, the Army Howitzer Type 4 was typical of the heavier field artillery of the period. The weapon's details included a weight of 6,160lb (2,794kg), calibre of 149.1mm (5.87in) with an L/14.6 barrel, length of 20ft 9in (6.325m), elevation and traverse arcs of –5 to +65 degrees and 3 degrees left and right of the centreline, rate of fire of four rounds per minute for two minutes declining to one round per minute thereafter, muzzle velocity of 1,345ft (410m) per second, maximum range of 10,465yds (9,570m), and detachment of six or seven. The weapon could fire a number of projectile types each weighing some 80lb (36.32kg), their recoil being absorbed by a hydro-pneumatic recoil system, and while the howitzer could be moved over short distances as a complete unit on its two iron-tyred spoked wooden wheels, the standard method of longer-distance transport was in two loads each drawn by six horses.

of longer-range targets or positions that are hidden by natural or man-made obstructions such as a hill or village, over which the shell can pass before plummeting toward its target.

During the enhancement of the overall capabilities of artillery, the two features that proved difficult to solve – but which were seminal to the creation of modern artillery – were accurate weapon laying with the long-ranged type of fire now possible, and a method to control the recoil of the gun. Up to this time, the simple iron sight and then the slightly more advanced tangent sight had been sufficient for aiming purposes, but with a range in excess of 4,000yds (3,660m) now possible, something better than basic eyesight was required. The answer was found in the gun-laying methods developed for the Royal Navy by Captain Percy Scott, namely the telescopic sight: this was a telescope with

The Italian 149mm (5.87in) gun was a piece of heavy field artillery optimised for use in inhospitable regions. The weapon's details included a weight of 17,857 lb (8,100kg), elevation arc of −10 to +35 degrees, rate of fire of two rounds per minute, muzzle velocity of 2,198ft (670m) per second, and maximum range of 7,380yds (6,750m) with a 92.6lb (42kg) shell.

cross wires, that was clamped in a suitable position on the gun carriage and coupled to the gun so that movement of the gun moved the sight. It was a simple yet sufficient method of laying the gun with considerable accuracy, and is still the standard method albeit in modernised form.

Recoil had been a major problem right from the beginning of artillery's history. With the exception of heavy siege artillery, which was usually delivered to its tactical position in disassembled form and then erected on a prepared and fixed site that could absorb the recoil forces, artillery was generally intended for tactical operations on the battlefield and therefore had to be as light and as mobile as possible. This meant that most pieces of artillery were based on a two-wheeled carriage with a trail that carried the eye by which the gun was pulled by horses or other draught animals, and which helped to stabilize the gun in firing position. Even with black powder propellant, however, the recoil forces were so great that the gun recoiled several feet as it was fired: this meant that before it could be fired again, the crew had to manhandle the weapon back into position and then, after reloading, re-lay the weapon. This was a time-consuming process that reduced gun batteries' rates of fire, especially in the type of sustained battle in which stamina became a critical factor: at the Battle of Waterloo in 1815, for instance, the British gunners became so exhausted that they were unable to manhandle their weapons back into position, and therefore reloaded and fired from the positions into which their guns had recoiled. As might be expected, this seriously affected the accuracy of the gunfire.

The recoil problem became more acute as propellants were made more powerful and as the construction of guns was improved to reduce their weight (for reduced cost and better tactical mobility, without sacrificing the barrel strength on which depended the integrity of the weapon and thus the safety of its crew). The effect of these changes was to increase the tendency of guns

The Skoda 7.5cm Gebirgskanone M.15 mountain gun/howitzer was one of the best such equipments available in World War I. The weapon's details included a weight of 1,352lb (613kg), calibre of 75mm (2.95in) with an L/15.4 barrel, elevation and traverse arcs of −10 to +50 degrees and 3.5 degrees left and right of the centreline, muzzle velocity of 1,149ft (350m) per second with the HE projectile or 804ft (245m) per second with the shrapnel projectile, and maximum range of 9,025yds (8,250m).

to recoil out of position, especially when these guns were carried on a wheeled carriage. Early in the nineteenth century a French officer, the Chevalier de Beaulieu, suggested a muzzle brake system in which a gas deflection device was installed in front of the muzzle to trap some of the forward-rushing propellant gases and thus draw the gun forward as a means of partly counteracting the recoil forces. Trials with muskets fitted with a muzzle brake proved moderately successful, but the technology of the day was inadequate to make the muzzle brake effective with pieces of artillery.

Even if it had worked, the muzzle brake would have been little more than a palliative, as the weight of current guns was so high that the shot had departed and the force of the propellant gases had been dissipated before the effect of a muzzle brake could make itself felt. This is not to deny that the muzzle brake can have its uses, as proved from the 1930s when such devices have been used with considerable success on more advanced weapons based on a comparatively lighter gun fitted with a recoil system of the type discussed below; even in such guns, however, the effect of the muzzle brake is an addition rather than an alternative to the main recoil system.

The problem of recoil was becoming acute in the 1860s. At this time the United Kingdom, suddenly made aware of the inadequacy of its coastal defences against a re-emergent threat of hostilities with France, was building additional defences and improving existing fortifications with better guns (although the guns' existing casemates lacked the size to accommodate the recoil of modern guns). The current system comprised an inclined ramp up which a standard naval gun recoiled on its carriage with four small wheels: if the recoil appeared excessive, the gunners strewed sand on the ramp to increase friction; and if the recoil seemed inadequate, the gunners spread grease on the ramp to reduce friction. Faced with the same problem, the Americans developed the so-called 'compressor' system in which a series of metal plates was hung between the sides of the slide to interleave with another series of plates extending below the gun carriage: a screw jack was used to adjust the friction between these two sets of plates and thereby control the length of the recoil. In the British system the gun was checked at the moment of maximum recoil by a block-and-tackle device, and in the American system by a flick of the screw jack; in each system the gun used gravity to rumble down the ramp into position after being reloaded.

It was a workable although extremely cumbersome system that placed considerable emphasis on the crew's knowledge of a particular gun. What was needed was an automatic and therefore more reliable system that placed no demands on crew experience. The answer was found in a hydraulic system.

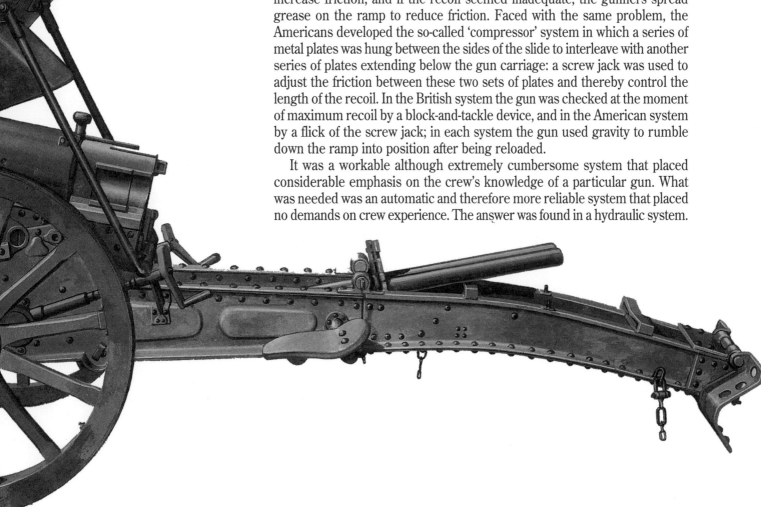

The Americans had already experimented with such a system: the recoiling gun ran back up its ramp until it struck a buffer piston rod, whereupon the buffer piston was driven back into the buffer cylinder in which water absorbed the recoil shock and brought the recoil to a halt. This system certainly achieved wonders in reducing the shock of the recoil, but did nothing to control or reduce recoil.

The hydraulic system provided the germ of an idea to a British team working at the Woolwich Arsenal under the supervision of Colonel Clerk. This team developed a new buffer system in which a cylinder of oil was attached to the ramp and the end of the piston rod was attached to the gun carriage: the piston head had a hole in it, and the recoil of the gun was controlled by the rate at which the oil passed from one side of the piston head to the other as the piston head moved through the oil. The system was still relatively primitive, but had the considerable advantages of not only stopping the recoil, but also of controlling the recoil and passing the recoil forces to the ramp and thus to the ground or the structure in which the gun was accommodated: this allowed the structure of the ramp (no longer required to carry the main recoil forces on its own) to be simplified and lightened with consequent improvements in the way it could be traversed, and also made it possible for the recoil of the gun to be controlled to the space available in existing casemates. It is worth noting, however, that the system included no provision for the gun to be returned automatically to battery, a task in which gravity, handspikes and the block and tackle still had to be employed.

This hydraulic buffer system was the basis of all future development in recoil systems, however, and was thus directly responsible for the evolution of the quick-firing gun which does not need to be re-laid between rounds. It was the quick-firing field gun that paved the way for developments in the years to come, and the type is therefore worthy of discussion in slightly greater detail.

The task set to designers in the creation of the quick-firing field gun was the production of a weapon that could achieve the maximum possible rate of fire under tactical conditions, and to this end the most desirable features were quickly established as unitary ammunition (the fused projectile crimped into the forward end of the brass case containing the propellant and its ignition system) so that the gun could be loaded quickly and simply as soon as the breech had been opened and the previous round's empty case extracted; a simple and fast-acting breech mechanism; an effective form of recoil control

The Russian 6in (152mm) howitzer of the World War I period was not an exceptional equipment, but was rugged, reliable and accurate.

Like other combatants in World War I, the Germans soon found themselves short of large-calibre field guns capable of firing at high velocity in the direct-fire role, and therefore adopted a similar expedient, namely a naval ordnance on a land carriage. This weapon was based on the gun originally designed as the secondary armament of German battleships, and its details included a weight of 25,408lb (11,525kg), calibre of 150mm (5.91in) with an L/40 barrel, elevation and traverse arcs of –8 to +32 degrees and 13.5 degrees left and right of the centreline, and maximum range of 19,000yds (17,375m) with the lighter of the two available projectiles.

An obsolete weapon that nonetheless served right through World War I was this French equipment in 120mm (4.72in) calibre. The gun was made in 1890, as suggested by its primitive recoil system.

so that the gun crew could remain in position round their weapon ready to reload as soon as the weapon had been fired; and some form of protection for the crew against the effects of small-arms fire and shell splinters.

Many weapons were designed and built in modest numbers as the artillery establishments of the world's most advanced nations sought to achieve this complex combination of features. The honours for being first to achieve this goal go to France, which standardised this Schneider weapon as the Canon de 75 modèle 1897. Generally known in the English-speaking world as the 'French 75', this gun was the result of a protracted evolutionary design process which incorporated a hydro-pneumatic recoil system that not only absorbed the gun's recoil but also returned the gun into battery after each shot; a quick-acting breech mechanism of the Nordenfeldt type (a breech block

mounted eccentrically to the bore's axis with a cutaway portion that, aligned with the bore, permitted loading but was then rotated to swing a solid section of the block into position behind the cartridge case); fixed ammunition of the unitary type; a shield to protect the crew; provision for the wheel brake shoes to be dropped under the wheels to hold the carriage firmly in position; a pole trail fitted with a spade that dug into the ground and further stabilized the carriage in firing position; and an independent sighting system that permitted the gunner to lay the gun while an assistant controlled elevation.

The 'French 75' set the standard against which all other pieces of field artillery would now be measured. The primary details of this weapon included a calibre of 75mm (2.95in) with an L/36 barrel (barrel length of 36 calibres), weight of 4,343lb (1,970kg) in travelling order reducing to 2,513lb (1,140kg) in action, elevation and traverse arcs on the carriage of −11 to +18 degrees and 3 degrees left and right respectively, and a range of 12,140yds (11,100m) with a 13.66lb (6.195kg) shell fired at a muzzle velocity of 1,886ft (575m) per second.

The real key to the success of the 'French 75' was its advanced system to handle the recoil and return the gun to battery. Early observers were amazed at the steadiness of the weapon while it was being fired at 15 rounds or more per minute. Other such systems were already available, but these were based on a simple buffer (to control recoil) and large springs (compressed during recoil and then expanded to return the gun to battery). The effect of this primitive combination was to cut off recoil abruptly and then slam the gun back into battery: the net result was that the gun still leaped or rolled backward, although not as far as would have been the case without this system. The 'French 75', on the other hand, recoiled smoothly for between 3 and 4ft (0.9 and 1.2m) before coming to a halt and then sliding gently but quickly back into battery without the carriage moving. As details of the 'French 75' reached other countries, its operation became known as the 'long recoil' system and was adopted virtually universally: by Vickers and Coventry Ordnance Works in the UK, Krupp in Germany, Bofors in Sweden, Skoda in Austria-Hungary, Cockerill in Belgium, Vickers-Terni and Ansaldo in Italy, Putilov in Russia, Osaka Arsenal in Japan, and Bethlehem in the USA.

A weapon introduced in 1917 and known to the British as the 'Screaming Lizzie' for the high-pitched wail of its high-velocity shell, this was the 10cm Feldkanone 17 with a barrel characterised by a calibre of 105mm (4.13in), L/45 length, elevation arc of between −2 and +45 degrees, and traverse arc of 3 degrees left and right of the centreline. The weapon weighed 7,276lb (3,300kg), and fired a 40.8lb (18.5kg) shell with a muzzle velocity of 2,130ft (650m) per second to achieve a maximum range of 18,050yds (16,505m), and was notably accurate.

The Austro-Hungarian army's standard heavy field howitzer was the Skoda-built 15cm schwere Feldhaubitze M.14 with a barrel of 149.1mm (5.87in) calibre and only L/14 length, elevation arc of –5 to +43 degrees, traverse arc of 2.5 degrees left and right of the centreline, weight of 5,168lb (2,345kg), muzzle velocity of 984ft (300m) per second to fire a 90.4lb (41kg) shell to a range of 7,550yds (6,905m), and detachment of eight.

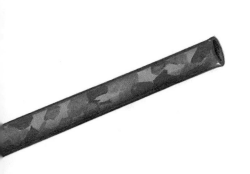

By the end of World War I (1914-18), the French pattern of quick-firing field gun had developed into a large number of weapons in calibres between 75mm (2.95in) and 105mm (4.13in). Among the classics of this breed were the German 77mm (3.03in) Feldkanone 16, 105mm Kanone 17/04 and 105mm Feldhaubitze 16; the Austro-Hungarian 76.5mm (3.012in) Skoda Kanone 17 and 100mm (3.94in) Skoda Kanone 14; and the British 76.2mm (3in) Ordnance, QF, 13pdr Gun and 83.8mm (3.3in) Ordnance, QF, 18pdr Gun used by the horse and field artillery respectively.

Further up the scale was heavy artillery with calibres in the range between 105mm (4.13in) and 210mm (8.27in). Despite their greater calibre, which ensured that a larger and heavier projectile could be fired to a considerably longer range than the smaller pieces of field artillery, these were conceptually related to the smaller-calibre weapons in their technical details. Being more massive, however, larger-calibre weapons were less mobile than their smaller-calibre counterparts, but came into their own later in World War I as the initial mobile operations gave way to attritional warfare after November 1914. The lines of parallel trenches had offered the soldiers of each side good protection against the direct fire of smaller-calibre weapons, but had placed greater emphasis on the more destructive capabilities provided by larger-calibre weapons. These fell into two classes, namely the larger-calibre guns that could engage point targets such as artillery dumps and the enemy's rear-area gun lines with direct fire at long range, and the larger-calibre howitzers that tackled front-line targets with plunging fire at somewhat shorter ranges.

The importance of these weapons grew as the static trench warfare of World War I dragged on, for up to the time of the tank's first appearance in September 1916, and its availability in substantial numbers from the summer of 1917, the only tactic that World War I commanders could imagine was the massive use of artillery. This was employed in great numbers and over protracted periods to lay down vast weights of fire designed to blast the enemy's trench lines, in preparation for the infantry assault that was designed to penetrate through the blasted section before the enemy could counterattack, and thereby create the gap into the enemy's rear areas that could be exploited by horsed cavalry (to cut the enemy's lines of communication and thereby facilitate the progress of the follow-up infantry).

Heavy guns and howitzers were essential to this process, and the middle stages of World War I were therefore dominated by these pieces of artillery. Good examples of such weapons were the Austro-Hungarian Skoda 149.1mm (5.87in) Haubitze 14 howitzer, Skoda 152.4mm (6in) Kanone 15/16 gun and Skoda 210mm (8.27in) Haubitze 18 howitzer; the French St Chamond 145mm (5.7in) Canon de 145L modèle 1916 gun, St Chamond 155mm (6.1in) Canon de 155L modèle 1916 gun, St Chamond 155mm Canon de 155C modèle 15 howitzer, St Chamond 155mm Canon de 155C modèle 1917 howitzer, and Filloux 155mm Canon de 155 Grande Puissance gun; the German 149.7mm (5.89in) schwere Feldhaubitze 13 howitzer, 149.3mm (5.878in) Kanone 16 gun, 152.4mm (6in) Haubitzen 09 and 10, and 211mm (8.3in) langer Mörser howitzer; the Italian 149.1mm (5.87in) Cannone da 149 gun; the British 4.5in (114.3mm) Ordnance, QF, Howitzer Mk I howitzer, 5in (127mm) Ordnance, BL, 60pdr Gun Mk I gun, 6in(152.4mm) Ordnance, BL, Gun Mk VIII gun, 6in Ordnance, BL, 6in 26cwt Howitzer Mk I howitzer, and 8in (203mm) Ordnance, BL, Howitzer Mk VII howitzer; and the American 155mm (6.1in) Howitzer M1918 howitzer.

Typical of these assorted weapons are the German Kanone 16, the British 60pdr gun and the American M1918 howitzer, the last an Americanised version of a French weapon, the Schneider Canon de 155C modèle 1917. The Kanone 16 was built in two almost identical versions by Krupp and Rheinmetall as the K 16 Kr with an L/42.7 barrel and the Kanone 16 Rh with an L/42.9 barrel: the details of the K 16 Kr included a weight of 22,445lb (10,180kg) in action, on-mounting elevation and traverse angles of 0 to +46 degrees and 4 degrees left and right respectively, and a range of 24,070yds (22,000m) with a 110.74lb (50.223kg) shell fired at a muzzle velocity of 2,440ft (744m) per second. The details of the 60pdr Gun Mk II gun, which was a post-war development of the 60pdr Gun Mk I, included a weight of 14,148lb (6,423kg) in travelling order and 12,048lb (5,470kg) in firing position, on-mounting elevation and traverse angles of –6 to +35 degrees and 4 degrees left and right respectively, and a range of 15,100yds (13,815m) with a 60lb (27.24kg) shell fired from the L/38.45 barrel with a muzzle velocity of 2,176ft (663m) per second. The details of the M1918 howitzer included a weight of 9,518lb

A thoroughly workmanlike weapon that survived right into World War II was the 15cm Kanone 16 Kr; the letters at the end indicating that this was the Krupp-built weapon that differed in slight details from the Rheinmetall-built 15cm Kanone 16 Rh. The details of this weapon, which was of moderately great importance in German operations during the later part of World War I, included a calibre of 149.3mm (5.878in), L/42.7 barrel length, weight of 22,445lb (10,180kg), elevation arc of between 0 and +46 degrees, traverse arc of 4 degrees left and right of the centreline, and muzzle velocity of 2,440ft (744m) per second to fire the 110.74lb (50.223kg) shell to a maximum range of 24,070yds (22,000m).

(4,321kg) in travelling order and 8,184lb (3,715kg) in firing position, on-mounting elevation and traverse angles of 0 to +42 degrees and 3 degrees left and right respectively, and a range of 12,295yds (11,250m) with a 94.27lb (42.8kg) shell fired from the L/13.64 barrel at a muzzle velocity of 1,478ft (451m) per second.

While most of the countries that would soon become embroiled in World War I were content in the first decade of the twentieth century to devote their artillery design and production efforts to such field artillery, the Germans and Austro-Hungarians appreciated that their longer-term offensive plans would require their armies to penetrate through bands of fixed defensive positions; therefore, they instructed their gun manufacturers to devote a significant part of their effort to the design and manufacture of modest numbers of heavy artillery pieces in the calibre range upward of 210mm (8.27in). These weapons were not designed for field use in mobile warfare, but rather for limited mobility or transport in dismantled state to the location of siege operations. The two most celebrated of these weapons were the Austro-Hungarian 'schlanke Emma' 305mm (12in) howitzer designed and built by Skoda, and the German 'dicke Bertha' 420mm (16.54in) howitzer designed and built by Krupp.

Both these weapons displayed prodigious capabilities in the task of penetrating and destroying concrete fortifications, and although there was little further demand for weapons of this specific type, especially as their mobility was so limited, further work on super-heavy artillery was based on wheeled carriages and later, as these became increasingly problematical with increasing gun calibre, on railway carriages. The British, for example, had been considering super-heavy artillery for some years, and the Coventry Ordnance Works 4.5in (114.3mm) howitzer was soon scaled up to 9.2in (233.7mm) calibre in a weapon that could be dismantled for movement on wagon bodies towed by steam traction engines. The weapon proved to be an excellent piece of ordnance through its combination of a durable barrel and considerable accuracy with a heavy shell. Further weapons, in calibres up to 15in (381mm), were produced by several of the combatants in semi-mobile gun and howitzer forms for dismantled movement or alternatively for installation on a railway carriage.

After World War I there was a considerable shift in the emphasis although not the technology of gun design, as national war ministries, which had become heavily involved in gun design during the war, were now loath to give up this capability. The effect was to reduce the gun design capabilities of manufacturers, who were now increasingly asked to implement the designs of the official design teams. Another change that was demanded at the highest

The 10.5cm leichte Feldhaubitze 13 was produced by Krupp, and its details included a calibre of 105mm (4.13in), L/20 barrel length, elevation arc of between −4 and +43 degrees, and a muzzle velocity of 1,410ft (430m) per second to fire a 35.34lb (16kg) shell to a maximum range of 9,735yds (8,900m).

military levels (but frequently not implemented as a result of financial stringencies during the 1920s and 1930s), was for larger-calibre guns: the tendency was therefore for medium field artillery to possess a calibre in the order of 85 to 105mm (3.34 to 4.13in) and for heavy field artillery to span the calibre bracket between 140 and 155mm (5.5 and 6.1in). An example of this tendency is provided by the British: the War Office decided that the army should adopt a 105mm weapon as its standard field howitzer, and the design of such a weapon was contracted to Vickers, which produced successful prototype weapons by 1930. At this point the Treasury stepped into the matter, objecting to the financial burden that would have to be suffered for the production and introduction of this wholly new weapon at a time when the army still had many hundreds of perfectly serviceable 18pdr (83.8mm/3.3in) guns. The final result was a compromise of the type so

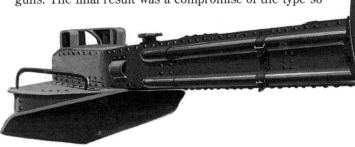

typical in British history. The War Office had its way about the need for a more advanced gun, and the Treasury achieved its wish to avoid large capital expenditure: from 1935, therefore, more than 1,000 of the 18pdr guns had their barrels bored out to take a new and larger round of ammunition firing a 25pdr shell of 87.6mm (3.45in) calibre. The revised weapon was the Ordnance, QF, 25pdr Gun Mk 1, which thus retained the 18pdr gun's carriage (in a form revised with pneumatically tyred wheels in place of the original wooden-spoked and steel-tyred wheels) and thereby saved considerable expenditure.

Generally known as the 18/25pdr gun, this weapon was limited in elevation to a maximum of 30 degrees by its retention of the 18pdr's Mk IIITP carriage with its pole trail, but later the Mk IVP carriage was adopted, this having a box trail whose central gap allowed the breech of the gun to be lowered farther for a maximum elevation angle slightly in excess of 37 degrees, and there was also the Mk VP carriage of the type originally developed for the 25pdr Gun Mk 2. On the Mk IVP carriage, the 18/25pdr gun had a weight of 3,570lb (1,621kg), on-mounting elevation and traverse angles of −5 to +37 degrees and 4.5 degrees left and right respectively, and a range of 12,000yds (10,875m) with a 25lb (11.34kg) shell fired from the L/28.13 barrel at a muzzle velocity of 1,706ft (520m) per second.

In 1936 the range requirement for this 'new' standard field artillery weapon was increased to 13,500yds (12,345m), but this was beyond the capabilities of the 18/25pdr conversion: the maximum elevation angle was too low for the generation of the maximum range possible with the ammunition, and the carriage lacked the strength to cope with the full-charge cartridge designed for the 25pdr round. The 18/25pdr therefore used a round with a reduced propellant charge, but the full capabilities of the round were finally permitted by the adoption of a new carriage to create the Ordnance, QF, 25pdr Gun Mk 2. As originally planned, this was to have been of the split-trail type allowing a larger angle of on-mounting traverse, but

Just entering British service in the summer of 1916, when it was blooded in the Battle of the Somme as replacement for the 6in 30cwt howitzer, the 6in 26cwt howitzer (more formally the BL, 6in 26cwt Howitzer, Mk I) proved to be a well-designed and well-made weapon admirably suited to the warfare of World War I. The details of this important weapon, of which some 4,000 were in service by the time of the Armistice in November 1918, included a calibre of 6in (152.4mm), an L/14.6 barrel, weight of 9,849lb (4,467kg), elevation arc of between 0 and +45 degrees, traverse arc of 4 degrees left and right of the centreline, and muzzle velocity of 1,409ft (429m) per second to fire the 100.19lb (45.44kg) shell to a maximum range of 11,400yds (10,425m).

Opposite: The German 15cm schwere Feldhaubitze 13 was one of the best pieces of field artillery to be used in World War I, and remained in service right through the 1920s and 1930s to see limited service in World War II. The details of the type included a calibre of 149.7mm (5.89in), an L/17 barrel, weight of 4,961lb (2,250kg), elevation arc of between −5 and +45 degrees, traverse arc of 4.5 degrees left and right of the centreline, and muzzle velocity of 1,250ft (381m) per second to fire the 89.96lb (40.8kg) shell to a maximum range of 9,410yds (8,605m).

after a number of early trials this Mk VP carriage was abandoned in favour of the Carriage Mk 1 with a humped box trail and a circular firing platform. The humped box trail was extremely strong and allowed a greater ordnance elevation angle, and the complete weapon could easily be located on a circular firing platform on which the wheels could be moved, permitting rapid traverse through 360 degrees.

The details of the 25pdr Gun Mk 2 included a weight of 3,968lb (1,801kg), on-mounting elevation and traverse angles of –5 to +40 degrees and 4 degrees left and right respectively, and a range of 13,400yds (12,255m) with a 25lb (11.34kg) shell fired from the L/28.25 barrel at a muzzle velocity of 1,745ft (532m) per second. The weapon entered service in 1940, at about the time of the British reverse in France in May of that year, and before the end of World War II (1939-45) more than 12,000 such weapons had been delivered. Able to fire in the direct and indirect modes, the 25pdr was really a gun/howitzer, and proved very popular for its rugged reliability, handiness and generally excellent performance. So good was the type, moreover, that few changes were made during the course of its production run: some weapons that had to double in the anti-tank role in the North African campaign were fitted with muzzle brakes to offset the recoil of the larger propellant charge used with the anti-tank projectile, the Mk 2 carriage was introduced as a narrowed version of the Mk 1 carriage for use in jungle warfare, and the Mk 3 carriage introduced a hinged trail to permit a higher angle of elevation for mountain warfare. The 25pdr remained in service with the British and many of their Commonwealth allies until well into the 1970s, and the weapon is still used in several parts of the world.

Even the most cursory examination of the 25pdr gun/howitzer reveals a major difference in the concept of this and contemporary weapons

compared with those of World War I: this was the adoption of some sort of system to improve the weapons' traverse angles. World War I weapons generally had been fitted with a pole trail that limited the elevation angle of the gun and, perhaps more importantly, meant that the on-mounting traverse angle had to be kept small as the triangular footprint of the equipments' narrow-track main wheels and spade-fitted pole trail provided only marginal stability to lateral movement. This was sufficient for the purposes of World War I and its generally static warfare, but found disfavour during the 1920s as the lessons of the war were analysed. All modern armies decided that trench warfare had been an aberration that would not be repeated for a number of reasons, including a determination to ensure that mobile warfare of the type made possible in World War I by the advent of the tank would be enhanced by the availability of more modern tanks and greater numbers of lorries, so that the infantry and artillery could be motorised.

The determination to ensure that any future war did not bog down into static trench conditions meant that the artillery would have to deal with point targets that were moving, often at right angles to the artillery's line of fire. The ability to engage targets of this crossing type was beyond the artillery equipments of World War I with their very limited on-mounting traverse angles and traverse rates. There were two possible solutions to the need for larger traverse angles. One was the adoption of a turntable so that the whole weapon could be turned rapidly to approximately the right bearing before the on-mounting traverse capability was brought into play, and this system was used by the British for the 25pdr gun/howitzer, whose box trail was conceptually related to the pole trail although the central gap allowed greater on-mounting elevation and traverse angles than had been common in World War I. The other solution was the adoption of a carriage with wider-track wheels and split trails: the latter were brought together for towed movement of the weapon (using an eye on the joined trails for smaller weapons or a special eye-fitted axle for larger equipments), and in firing position were spread to their maximum width to provide a larger and therefore more stable firing footprint that could permit large on-mounting traverse angles without overturning as the gun was fired.

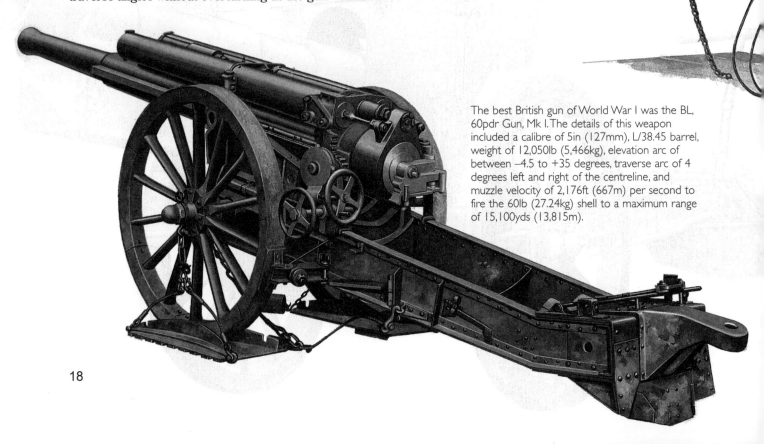

The best British gun of World War I was the BL, 60pdr Gun, Mk I. The details of this weapon included a calibre of 5in (127mm), L/38.45 barrel, weight of 12,050lb (5,466kg), elevation arc of between −4.5 to +35 degrees, traverse arc of 4 degrees left and right of the centreline, and muzzle velocity of 2,176ft (667m) per second to fire the 60lb (27.24kg) shell to a maximum range of 15,100yds (13,815m).

The static nature of World War I made feasible the use of virtually immobile super-heavy howitzers for the massive bombardment of key positions. Typical of this breed was the British 15in Howitzer Mk I, of which 12 were ordered by Winston Churchill, during November 1914. The weapons that were completed (six were in France at the time of the Armistice) fired 25,300 rounds and were manned by the men of the Royal Marine Howitzer Brigade. The details of these massive equipments included a calibre of 15in (381mm), a 1,450lb (658kg) shell fired to a maximum range of 10,000yds (9,145m), and a detachment of 12.

To complement the 25pdr gun, which was at best a medium field artillery piece and, as a result of the financial interference mentioned above, somewhat smaller in calibre than the equivalent weapons in service with countries such as Germany and the USA, the British operated a number of heavier field artillery weapons, including improved World War I howitzers as well as two more modern guns in the forms of the Ordnance, BL, 4.5in Gun Mk 2 and the Ordnance, BL, 5.5in Gun Mk 3. The 4.5in (114.3mm) weapon had its origins in the mid-1930s, when 76 Ordnance, BL, 4.5in Gun Mk I equipments were produced as new barrels on the modified carriage of the 60pdr gun of World War I, adapted with pneumatically tyred wheels with brakes. Further development led to the Mk II version with an improved version of the Mk I's ordnance on a derivative of the excellent carriage designed for the larger 5.5in (139.7mm) gun. The Mk II weapon proved

The Germans' super-heavy 'dicke Bertha' (fat Bertha) howitzers were semi-mobile equipments specially designed for the destruction of major fortifications, and proved admirably suited to this task as revealed by their demolition of the Belgian forts in 1914. The equipment had a calibre of 420mm (16.54in) and weighed 75 tons (76.2 tonnes), and was grouped in two-howitzer batteries with a strength of 280 men. The howitzer could fire ten 2,052lb (930kg) shells at the rate of 10 per hour to a maximum range of 15,530yds (14,200m).

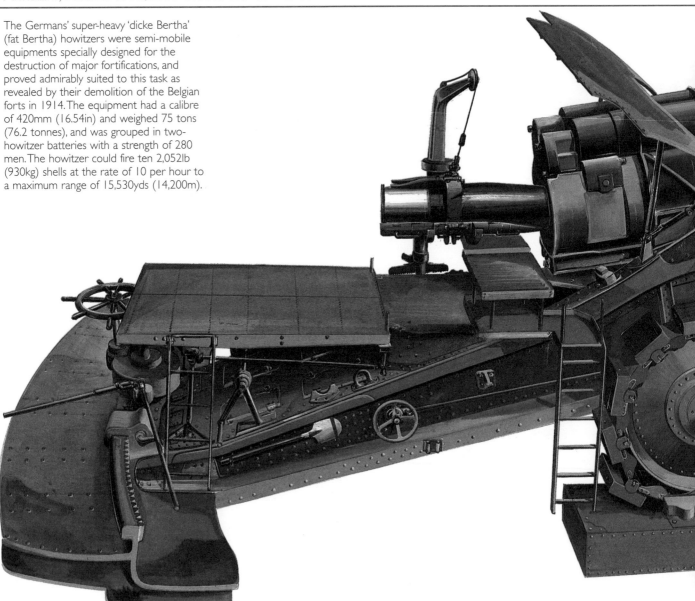

accurate and long-ranged, but was hampered by the small explosive filling of its 55lb (24.97kg) shell. Relatively few of these weapons (intended mainly for the counter-battery and interdiction roles) were made, as greater capability was provided by the 5.5in weapon.

The origins of this weapon can also be found in the mid-1930s, when the War Office issued a requirement for a new gun firing a 100lb (45.4kg) shell to a range of 16,000yds (14,630m). Design work on such a weapon was well advanced when in 1939 the War Office decided that a calibre of 5.5in rather than a shell weight of 100lb should be the critical factor; even so, the first such weapons were test-fired in 1940, soon revealing that the carriage designed for the originally planned 5in weapon was too light to handle the recoil forces of the 5.5in weapon. This led to delays in the production programme until a new carriage could be designed, and the 5.5in weapon finally entered service in 1941. The type then proved to be highly successful and examples of this weapon, which was in fact a gun/howitzer, remained in British service until the late 1970s. The details of the 5.5in gun included a weight of 12,768lb (5,796kg), on-mounting elevation and traverse angles of −5 to +45 degrees and 30 degrees left and right respectively, and a range of 16,200yds (14,815m) with an 80lb (36.32 kg) shell fired from the L/31.2

barrel at a muzzle velocity of 1,675ft (510m) per second; there was also a heavier 100lb shell that could be fired only to a shorter range.

The UK's main ally in World War II was the USA, which had devoted considerable thought and effort to the development of an effective artillery force in the 1920s and 1930s. As a result, the US Army's artillery arm was very ably equipped in World War II, with the 105mm Howitzer M2A1 as the main strength of its field artillery branch and its heavier units equipped mainly with the 155mm Howitzer M1, 155mm Gun M1918, 8in Howitzer M1, and 8in Gun M1.

The 105mm M2 howitzer was one of the main weapons proposed in 1919 by the Westerveldt Board, established immediately after World War I to consider ways in which the US Army's artillery arm could be improved in the light of its experiences in the war. The Board felt that the 75mm (2.95in) Field Gun M1917, the American copy of the 'French 75', was adequate in the short term for the battlefield direct-fire role, but thought that a larger-calibre howitzer would prove a useful adjunct. The truth of this conclusion was borne out by subsequent events, for the 105mm howitzer proved itself to be one of the classic weapons of World War II. In the short term, however, progress with the design and development of this weapon was painfully slow as a result of the severe financial restrictions imposed on the US military in the 1920s and early 1930s. It was only in 1939 that the design was finally completed by the Ordnance Department, but thereafter, progress was rapid. The weapon was placed in production during 1940, and up to the end of World War II some 8,536 such equipments were produced for use with the excellent split-trail M2A2 carriage, which was very sturdy and fitted with pneumatically tyred wheels on a number of self-propelled mountings. The details of this important weapon, which was used in every theatre involving American troops and could fire a useful 13 different types of projectile, included a weight of 4,260lb (1,934kg), on-mounting elevation and traverse angles of –5 to +65 degrees and 23 degrees left and right respectively, and a range of 12,500yds (11,430m) with the 33lb (14.98kg) shell fired from the L/22.5 barrel with a muzzle velocity of 1,550ft (473m) per second.

The 155mm Howitzer M1 was the heavier counterpart to the 105mm weapon, and was designed with extreme speed from 1939 by the Rock Island Arsenal for production from 1942. Up to 1945, 4,035 such equipments had been completed for service in every theatre involving American troops. Such was the success of the type, which soon acquired an excellent reputation for accuracy over its full range bracket, that it was retained in full service after the end of World War II with the revised designation M114, and is still in widespread service in many parts of the world. The weapon was extremely reliable, especially in its M1A1 version made of stronger steel, and was carried on the M1 carriage with pneumatically tyred wheels and a split-trail arrangement. The details of this weapon included a weight of 11,966lb (5,432kg), on-mounting elevation and traverse angles of –2 to +65 degrees and 26.5 degrees left and right respectively, and a range of

The Germans' 2.8cm schwere Panzerbüchse 41 was one of the most innovative weapons of World War II as it made use of the taper-bore barrel that decreased in calibre from 28mm at the breech to 20mm at the muzzle, to allow the pressure of the expanding propellant gases to work on an increasingly small base area and so accelerate the projectile to a muzzle velocity of 4,599ft (1,402m) per second.

The American 75mm Pack Howitzer M1A1 was an extremely compact weapon that could be broken down into nine loads for parachute delivery or animal transport over inhospitable terrain. The type was widely used in World War II, especially in regions such as Italy and the Pacific islands, and its details included a calibre of 75mm (2.95in), L/15.93 barrel, weight of 1,340lb (608kg), elevation arc of between –5and +45 degrees, traverse arc of 3 degrees left and right of the centreline, and muzzle velocity of 1,250ft (381m) per second to fire the 13.76lb (6.24kg) shell to a maximum range of 9,760yds (8,925m).

16,000yds (14,630m) with a 95lb (43.14kg) shell fired from the L/20 barrel at a muzzle velocity of 1,850ft (564m) per second. One of the primary operational advantages of this weapon was the fact that, like its smaller 105mm counterpart, it could fire a wide range of projectile types to suit the particular tactical requirements.

The 155mm Gun M1918 was an American development of the 155mm Gun M1917, which was the American designation for a French weapon, the Filloux Canon de 155 Grande Puissance, of which a substantial number were transferred in the last part of World War I. The M1918 was the American-built version, and during the 1930s the type was revised with a more modern carriage in the form of the generally similar M2 and M3 units, designed for high-speed towing and therefore fitted with more modern wheels characterised by pneumatic tyres and pneumatic brakes. The details of this weapon included a weight of 25,550lb (11,589kg) in travelling order and about 20,100lb (9,117kg) in firing position, on-mounting elevation and traverse angles of 0 to +35 degrees and 30 degrees left and right respectively, and a range of 20,100yds (18,380m) with a 94.71lb (43kg) shell fired from the L/36.4 barrel with a muzzle velocity of 2,360ft (720m) per second.

Although built only in smaller numbers – 1,006 and 130 respectively – the 8in Howitzer M1 and Gun M1 were potent long-range weapons: the howitzer was well known for its long-range accuracy and good capability against concrete fortifications, while the gun was a very accurate long-range bombardment weapon. The howitzer was designed by the Hughes Tool Company on the basis of the British 8in Howitzer Mk VIII (numbers of which had been supplied to the US Army in World War I and remained in service up to 1940), and entered service in 1942 on a very substantial carriage with large split trails (carried in the towing position by a two-wheeled single axle) and two four-wheel axles. The details of this impressive equipment, which was retained in service after World War II with the revised designation M114, included a weight of 32,005lb (14,515kg) in travelling order and 29,703lb (13,471kg) in firing position, on-mounting traverse angles of –2 to +64 degrees and 30 degrees left and right respectively, and a range of 18,510yds (16,925m) with a 200lb (90.7kg) shell fired from the L/25 barrel with a muzzle velocity of 1,950ft (594m) per second.

The Gun M1 was a considerably more substantial weapon, and was first demanded by the Westerveldt Board in 1919, although financial restrictions meant that work on such a weapon was halted in 1924 for resumption only in 1939. The weapon was standardised in 1941 for service from 1942 as a massive equipment fired on a split-trail carriage installed on the ground after delivery by special transport wagons in disassembled form for erection with the aid of a 20-ton crane. The details of this impressive weapon included a weight of 69,300lb (31,434kg), on-mounting elevation and traverse angles of –10 to +50 degrees and 20 degrees left and right respectively, and a range of 32,025yds (29,285m) with a 240.37lb (109.03kg) shell fired from the L/50 barrel with a muzzle velocity of 2,950ft (899m) per second.

The other main exponent of artillery on the Allied side in World War II was the USSR, which had inherited a considerable capability in the design and tactical employment of artillery from Russia. (Russia had failed to exploit this capability to its best advantage during World War I because of ammunition shortages and the ineptitude of its generals). The equipments most widely used in World War I and retained in service thereafter, often in updated forms, were the 76.2mm (3in) Putilov Field Gun Model 1902, 107mm (4.21in) Field Gun Model 1910, 121.9mm

(4.8in) Field Howitzer Model 1910, 152.4mm Field Gun Model 1910, and 152.4mm Putilov Field Howitzer Model 1909.

With the worst of the economic problems resulting from the 1917 Bolshevik Revolution and subsequent civil war over by the mid-1930s, the Soviets decided that the time was ripe for the development of a new generation of artillery equipments to replace the updated versions of the weapons procured by the Russians before and during World War I. The result was a series of weapons that were generally highly impressive in their capabilities and therefore retained in service well after the end of World War II. The smallest of the new weapons was the 76.2mm Field Gun Model 1936 that was introduced to service in 1939 with details that included a weight of 5,291lb (2,400kg) in travelling order and 2,976lb (1,350kg) in firing position, on-mounting elevation and traverse angles of –5 to +75 degrees and 30 degrees left and right respectively, and a range of 14,850yds (13,580m) with a 14.11lb (6.4kg) shell fired from the L/43 barrel with a muzzle velocity of 2,316ft (706m) per second. This weapon was the mainstay of the Soviet field artillery units in the first part of the 'Great Patriotic War', as the Soviets called their part of World War II. In the later part of the war, the Model 1936 gun was supplemented and then largely supplanted by the classic 76.2mm Field Gun Model 1942 that was otherwise known as the SiS-3. This was basically a development of the Model 1936 gun with a muzzle brake and split pole trails for reduced weight, and the result was a weapon that was reliable,and potent for its calibre. The Model 1942 remained in widespread service to the late 1970s, and its details included a weight of 2,469lb (1,120kg), on-mounting elevation and traverse angles of –5 to +37 degrees and 27 degrees left and right respectively, and a range of 14,545yds (13,300m) with a 13.69lb (6.21kg) shell fired from the L/39.3 barrel with a muzzle velocity of 2,231ft (680m) per second.

The British BL, 5.5in Gun Mk III was an excellent piece of equipment introduced in the early part of World War II and remaining in limited service into the later 1970s. The details of this very popular and successful piece of heavy artillery included a calibre of 5.5in (139.7mm), L/31.2 barrel, weight of 12,768lb (5,792kg), elevation arc of between –5 and +45 degrees, traverse arc of 30 degrees left and right of the centreline, and muzzle velocity of 1,675ft (510m) per second to fire the 80lb (36.32kg) lightweight of two HE shell types to a maximum range of 16,200yds (14,813m).

During World War II, the Soviets decided that the artillery barrages with which they prefaced their offensives required a slightly heavier component at the lighter end of the scale, and the result was a pair of excellent weapons in 85mm (3.35in) calibre. These were the Field Gun Model 1943 and the Field Gun Model 1944, the latter otherwise known as the D-44. The Model 1943 weapon was produced in relatively modest numbers, and although generally classified as a divisional gun was in fact used mainly in the anti-tank role. The weapon's primary details included a weight of 3,757lb (1,704kg), on-mounting elevation and traverse angles of 0 to +40 degrees and 15 degrees left and right respectively, and a range of 18,155yds (16,600m) with a 20.95lb (9.5kg) shell fired from the L/55 barrel with a muzzle velocity of 2,608ft (795m) per second. Produced in far larger numbers and still used in many parts of the world, the Model 1944 weapon introduced a muzzle brake and split pole trails, and its salient details included a weight of 3,804lb (1,725kg), on-mounting elevation and traverse angles of –5 to +40 and 27 degrees left and right respectively, and a range of 16,950yds (15,500m) with a 20.95lb shell fired from the L/55 barrel with a muzzle velocity of 2,608ft per second.

A higher calibre for Soviet weapons produced in large numbers for the field artillery role was 121.9mm (4.8in). The first Soviet-designed weapon in this calibre was the Field Gun Model 1931 with a weight of 17,199lb (7,800kg) in travelling order and 15,656lb (7,100kg) in firing position, on-mounting elevation and traverse angles of —4 to +45 degrees and 28 degrees left and right respectively, and a range of 22,825yds (20,870m) with a 55.1lb (25kg) shell fired from the L/45 barrel with a muzzle velocity of 2,625ft (800m) per second. The ordnance of this equipment was later added to the carriage of the 152.4mm (6in) Gun/Howitzer Model 1937 to create the Field Gun Model 1931/37 otherwise known as the A-19.

Another weapon in the same 121.9mm calibre was the Field Howitzer Model 1938 that was one of the most important equipments of its type in Soviet service right through World War II. This weapon's primary details included a weight of 6,174lb (2,800kg) in

A powerful but little-known weapon, the Germans 21cm lange Mörser was introduced in the period before World War I as a heavy howitzer, and among the few known details of the type are a calibre of 210mm (8.27in) and a maximum range of between 10,280yds (9,400m) with the 1914 short shell and 11,155yds (10,200m) with the 1896 long shell.

travelling order and 5,402lb (2,450kg) in firing position, on-mounting elevation and traverse angles of –3 to +63 degrees and 24.5 degrees left and right respectively, and a range of 12,910yds (11,800m) with a 47.98lb (21.76kg) shell fired from the L/21.9 barrel at a muzzle velocity of 1,690ft (515m) per second.

Next up the Soviet calibre ladder was 152.4mm (6in). An excellent weapon in this calibre was the Gun/Howitzer Model 1937, otherwise known as the ML-20 and intended for the counter-battery role on two types of carriage: one had spoked wooden wheels and was intended for horse traction, and the other had double-tyred steel wheels for tractor towing. The details of this weapon, which remained in service up to the 1980s, included a weight of 17,485lb (7,930kg) in travelling order and 15,717lb (7,128kg) in firing position, on-mounting elevation and traverse angles of –2 to +65 degrees and 29 degrees left and right respectively, and a range of 18,880yds (17,265m) with a 96.05lb (43.56kg) shell fired from an L/29 barrel at a muzzle velocity of 2,149ft (655m) per second.

The 152.4mm calibre bracket was completed by two other first-class weapons in the form of the Field Howitzer Model 1938 otherwise known as the M-10, and the Field Howitzer Model 1943 otherwise known as the D-1. The Model 1938 was designed from the outset for mechanical traction and featured a single axle with two double wheels, and its main details included a weight of 10,033lb (4,500kg) in travelling order and 9,150lb (4,150kg) in firing position, on-mounting elevation and traverse angles of –1 to +65 degrees and 25 degrees left and right respectively, and a range of 13,565yds (12,400m) with a 112.6lb (51.5kg) shell fired from the L/23.15 barrel at a muzzle velocity of 1,417ft (432m) per second, although the weapon could also be used in the anti-tank role with an 88.18lb (40kg) shot fired at 1,667ft (508m) per second. The Model 1943, which is still in moderately widespread service, was basically the carriage of the Model 1938 with a new ordnance carrying a double-baffle muzzle brake. The details of this weapon included a weight of 8,008lb (3,635kg) in travelling order and 7,940lb (3,600kg) in firing position, on-mounting elevation and traverse angles of –3 to +63

One of the many pieces of excellent artillery introduced by the Soviets in World War II was the 76.2mm Field Gun Model 1942, otherwise known as the SiS-3 and a development of the Model 1939 gun with a muzzle brake and a new carriage of the split-trail type with pole legs. The result was a light and therefore useful weapon that found considerable favour with the Soviet Army, which received the type in very large numbers for service into the late 1970s.

degrees and 17.5 degrees left and right respectively, and a range of 13,565yds with a 112.6lb shell fired from the L/24.6 barrel with a muzzle velocity of 1,667ft (508m) per second.

The largest of the standard Soviet artillery equipments used in World War II was the 203mm (8in) Howitzer Model 1931 otherwise known as the B-4. This was an enormous weapon produced in six variants, and was most notable for its tracked rather than wheeled carriage. The variants were differentiated mainly by the type of carriage and suspension used, but invariable details included on-mounting elevation and traverse angles of 0 to +60 degrees and 4 degrees left and right respectively, and a shell weight of 220.46lb (100kg) fired from the L/24 barrel at a muzzle velocity of between 1,765 and 1,991ft (538 and 607m) per second for a range of between 14,000 and 17,500yds (12,800 and 16,000m).

Of Germany, Italy and Japan, the three main combatants of the Axis forces ranged against the Allies in World War II, it was only Germany that made and operated high-quality artillery equipment, which often included weapons captured from the Allied powers. The smallest of the equipments operated by the Germans was the 105mm (4.13in) leichte Feldhaubitze (leFH) 18, which was designed by Rheinmetall and entered service in 1935. Although it was a reliable and rugged weapon with a number of modern features including split trails and a shield, it was given a faintly obsolescent appearance by the use of large steel-tyred wheels. The equipment had a weight of 5,589lb (2,535kg) in travelling order and 4,377lb (1,985kg) in firing position, on-mounting elevation and traverse angles of −6 to +40 degrees and 28 degrees left and right respectively, and a range of 11,675yds (10,675m) with a 32.65lb (14.81kg) shell fired from the L/25.8 barrel with a muzzle velocity of 1,542ft (470m) per second. The leFH 18 was undoubtedly a fine weapon in its basic capabilities, but there could be little doubt that it was also somewhat too heavy, as was made abundantly clear from the autumn of 1941 on the Eastern Front, where appallingly muddy Russian conditions often resulted in leFH 18 equipments becoming bogged down. In March 1942 the German army called for a weapon offering the same ballistic capabilities as the leFH 18 but with a considerably lighter overall weight without any sacrifice of strength, and the result was the leFH 18/40 which comprised the ordnance of the leFH 18 on a modified version of the carriage designed originally for the 75mm PaK 40 anti-tank guns. The le FH 18/40 initially retained the PaK 40's wheels, but later in the type's career these wheels

Not a piece of artillery in essence, but offering the German army of World War II some of its capabilities at a fraction of the cost, the 15cm Nebelwerfer 41 was a pioneering rocket launcher. The weapon weighed only 1,245lb (565kg) for towing on its two wheels, and was stabilized in firing position by the opening of its two pole-type trail legs and the lowering of the foot forward of the axle. The assembly of six 6.24in (158.5mm) barrels could be elevated through an arc between 5 and 45 degrees and traversed through an arc of 13.5 degrees left and right of the centreline, and could fire its six Wurfgranate 41 Spreng rockets in a rippled salvo at two-second intervals. This rocket weighed 70lb (31.8kg) with a 5.5lb (2.5kg) explosive load, and left the muzzle of the launch tube with a velocity of 1,120ft (342m) per second to reach a maximum range of 7,725yds (7,065m).

were replaced by units of greater diameter and increased width to reduce the tendency to bog down. The details of the leFH 18/40 included a weight of 4,310lb (1,955kg), on-mounting elevation and traverse angles of –6 to +40 degrees and 28 degrees left and right respectively, and a range of 13,485yds (12,325m) with a 32.65lb shell fired from the L/25.8 barrel with a muzzle velocity of 1,771ft (540m) per second.

The next German calibre was 128mm (5.04in), and in this calibre the Germans used small numbers of an exceptional weapon, the Kanone 44. This was developed in direct response to the Germans' belated realisation that, in general, the artillery of the Soviet army was superior not only in quantitative but also in qualitative terms to that of the German army. With a weight of 22,403lb (10,160kg) in firing position, the K 44 entered service in 1944 as a substantial direct- and indirect-fire weapon, really a gun/howitzer and anti-tank gun rather than just a gun, based on a large carriage supported when travelling by the four or six of two or three axles (on the more common Krupp or less common Rheinmetall versions respectively), and in firing position by two screw jacks under the axles and two outrigger legs that were extended from the sides of the carriage before large pads were extended to the ground by actuation of a screw system. This carriage carried the ordnance behind a substantial shield on a mounting that provided traverse through 360 degrees and elevation between –7.5 and +45 degrees. The ordnance was fitted with a 'pepperpot' muzzle brake, and fired a 62.4lb (28.3kg) HE shell or anti-tank shot from

27

the L/51.75 barrel with a muzzle velocity of 3,018ft (920m) per second for a range of 26,710yds (24,415m).

The following German calibre was 150mm (5.91in), and in this calibre the Germans had a number of important weapons. The most numerous of these, and the standard heavy howitzer of the German armies throughout World War II, was the schwere Feldhaubitze (sFH) 18 with an ordnance designed by Rheinmetall on a Krupp-designed carriage. The sFH 18 was designed from 1926 and entered service in 1935 as a weapon that combined modern features with the type of apparently obsolete wheel that was standard in the German army: this was a solid steel unit, pierced with holes to reduce weight, of considerable diameter and surrounded by a solid rubber tyre. The carriage was of the split-trail type, the ends of the closed trails being carried on a small two-wheel limber for towing by horses or a tractor. The tactical versatility of this equipment was increased by the availability of several different types of projectile within the separate-loading ammunition, but when it became clear in 1942 that the sFH 18 was considerably outranged by Soviet artillery equipments, the ordnance was modified to accept two charges additional to the standard six. This modification certainly boosted range to the required figure, but also shortened barrel life and strained the recoil system. The weapon was therefore further adapted with a renewable chamber liner and a muzzle brake to become the sFH 18(M). The primary details of the sFH 18 included a weight of 12,154lb (5,512kg) in firing position, on-mounting elevation and traverse angles of –3 to +45 degrees and 32 degrees left and right respectively, and a range of 14,600yds (13,325m) with a 95.7lb (43.5kg) shell fired from the L/29.6 barrel at a maximum muzzle velocity of 1,710ft (521m) per second.

The gun counterparts to the sFH 18 were the Kanone 18 and Kanone 39. The K 18 was designed from 1933 by Rheinmetall and entered service in 1938 as a basically sound weapon whose efficiency in tactical operations was somewhat hindered by the fact that the gun had to be towed in two sections (involving considerable effort and delay in the process of getting the gun into and out of action), and was given 360-degree traverse capability by the provision of a two-piece platform onto which the gun had to be towed before

The Bofors 40L70 a development of the weapon that had proved so successful in World War II in a host of land-based and shipborne forms. The basic weapon seen here has been further developed into a number of more advanced forms with an on-mounting power supply and fire-control systems (fair- and all-weather types), but the core details of this system, which is based on a four-wheeled carriage for towing but is stabilized in firing position by four screw jacks (two of them on lateral outriggers), include an L/70 barrel with a calibre of 40mm, weight of 11,354lb (5,150kg), length of 23ft 11in (7.29m), elevation arc of between –4 and +90 degrees, traverse angle of 360 degrees, rate of fire of 240 (or in later models) 300 rounds per minute (cyclic), range of 13,670yds (12,500m) horizontal maximum and 4,375yds (4,000m) slant effective, and detachment of four to six.

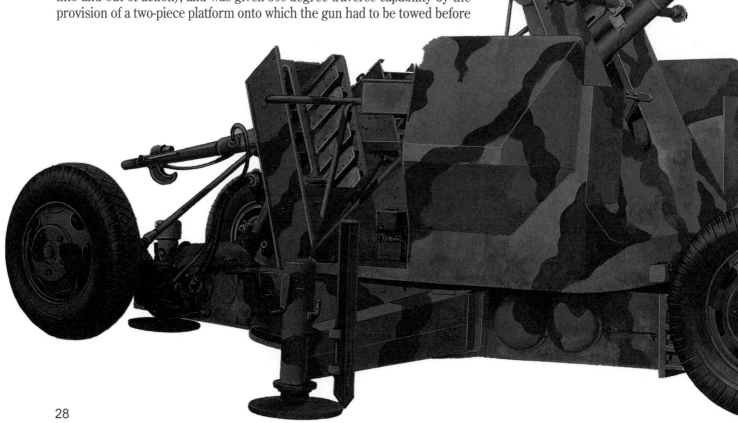

use. Details of this weapon included a weight of 28,131lb (12,760kg) in firing position, on-mounting elevation and traverse angles of –2 to +45 degrees and 5 degrees left and right respectively, and a range of 26,800yds (24,500m) with a 94.8lb (43kg) shell fired from the L/55 barrel with a muzzle velocity of 2,920ft (890m) per second; the type could also fire a special 95.9lb (43.5kg) shell for the penetration of concrete fortifications.

The K 39, which was used in smaller numbers, was a Krupp weapon originally designed for Turkey as a dual-role heavy field gun and coast-defence gun. The weapon was even more cumbersome than the K 18, having to be broken down into three loads for movement, and in firing position was installed on a portable turntable for 360-degree traverse. The location of the gun on this turntable was a laborious and slow process requiring a large amount of digging. The main details of the K 39 included a weight of 26,901lb (12,200kg), on-mounting elevation and traverse angles of –3 to +46 degrees and 30 degrees left and right respectively, and a range of 27,025yds (24,700m) with a 94.8lb shell fired from the L/55 barrel with a muzzle velocity of 2,838ft (865m) per second.

Entering service in 1941 and planned as a weapon to replace the German army's current 150 and 210mm (5.91 and 8.27in) guns, the 170mm (6.7in) Kanone 18 in Mörserlafette was a Krupp design using the same carriage as the Mrs 18 and the same recoil system as the K 38 (described below). The 170mm weapon proved to be an excellent piece of artillery, but demand constantly outstripped production and the weapon could not be employed as widely as had been hoped. The carriage was of the split-trail type with a single two-wheeled axle, and the primary details of the weapon included a weight of 38,632lb (17,520kg) in firing position, on-mounting elevation and traverse angles of 0 to +50 degrees and 8 degrees left and right respectively, and a range of 32,370yds (29,600m) with a 138.5lb (62.8kg) shell fired from the L/50 barrel with a muzzle velocity of 3,035ft (925m) per second; there was also a heavier and more destructive 149.9lb (68kg) shell for use at shorter ranges.

The largest standard calibre for German artillery was 210mm (8.27in), and in this bracket were two weapons in the form of the Mörser (Mrs)18 and Kanone 38. The Mrs 18 was a Krupp design that used basically the same carriage as the 170mm Kanone 18. This carriage had two variants (one with two wheels carrying solid rubber tyres and the other with four wheels carrying pneumatic tyres), and the main details of this powerful weapon included a weight of 36,824lb (16,700kg) in firing position, on-mounting elevation and traverse angles of 0 to +70 degrees and 8 degrees left and right (increasing to 360 degrees when the whole equipment was placed on the special trail platform that allowed a single man to move the weapon), and a range of 18,270yds (16,700m) with a 266.8lb (121kg) shell fired from the L/31 barrel with a muzzle velocity of 1,854ft (565m) per second. The versatility of this weapon was considerably enhanced by the availability of several types of projectile (including a 285.3lb/129.4kg concrete-penetrating shell, a muzzle stick bomb, and the Röchling fin-stabilized shell) and a six-charge propellant system that offered a range capability upward of 3,280yds (3,000m).

The K 38 was another Krupp design, in this instance ordered in 1938 as eventual replacement for the Mrs 18 that did not completely fulfil the German army's requirement. The guns were to have been delivered from 1940, but in fact the weapons were delivered after this time and only seven had been completed before production was terminated in 1943. Despite this fact, the K 38 was a highly advanced and efficient weapon with features from the Krupp 170 and 210mm guns, including a dual-recoil system that comprised the standard barrel recoil system and a system installed on the gun platform to allow this unit to recoil along slides on the upper part of the trail. The weapon was broken down into two loads but could be emplaced using only hand-operated winches installed on the carriage, and the on-mounting traverse angle could be increased to 360 degrees by installation of the equipment on a large platform. The details of this impressive weapon included a weight of 55,787lb (25,300kg), on-mounting elevation and traverse angles of 0 to +50 degrees and 8.5 degrees left and right respectively, and a range of 37,075yds (33,900m) with a 265lb (120kg) shell fired from the L/55.5 barrel with a muzzle velocity of 2,970ft (905m) per second.

In World War II, towed artillery had reached a conceptual peak which was not readily exceeded in the period following the war. In the immediate aftermath of the war, the victorious Allies inevitably decided that armies should retain the equipments that had proved successful and which were still available in numbers larger than required by the smaller peacetime armies. Thus it was only in the late 1950s and early 1960s that significant development of the towed gun and howitzer was resumed in earnest, the concentration now being placed on 155mm (6.1in) as the primary calibre for field as well as heavier artillery. There was little conceptually new about the equipments that now began to reach the production stage, for the type of weapon that had performed well in World War II was still advanced enough for its purposes, so the emphasis of design and development was placed on improving the breed rather than evolving something completely new. The improvements that were effected were based on features such as better materials for high strength-weight ratios; increased durability in items such as barrels; more reliable and sophisticated recoil systems including more effective muzzle brakes; upgraded fire-control systems for improved accuracy in long-range fire; and a wider assortment of specialised projectiles (including nuclear rounds and also cargo-carrying rounds that dispense submunitions towards the end of the trajectory for the purpose of creating minefields or attacking individual members of an armoured formation) to make artillery more flexible in its tactical applications. This has been a continuing process and, even more recently, other changes have included longer barrels to allow the build-up of the higher pressures required for the additional muzzle velocity that produces greater projectile range; superior propellants that also contribute to increased range and burn more steadily

Left: The 210mm (8.27in) rail gun developed by the Germans was intended as a long-range bombardment weapon, but proved itself an impractical weapon and saw virtually no operational employment.

Opposite: Designed by Krupp in 1937, the 'Gustav Gerät' was an enormous German rail gun with a calibre of 280mm (11.02in) named in honour of Gustav von Bohlen und Krupp, but was generally known as the 'Dora Gerät' as German artillerymen preferred to give their equipments female names. This fact has often led to the suggestion that there were in fact two such guns, but this is definitely not the case. The whole equipment weighed 1,350 tons in firing order and was moved piecemeal to its operational position, where a dual track was laid and the gun mount was built up with the aid of an overhead crane in a process that took nearly six weeks! The gun was assembled, maintained, guarded and operated by a 1,420-man detachment under the command of a major general, and was provided with two types of shell. These were a smaller HE shell fired to a maximum range of 51,400 yards (47,000m) and a larger concrete-piercing shell fired to a maximum range of 22,965 yards (21,000m). The only two occasions on which it is known that the gun was used operationally were in the siege of Sevastopol in 1942 and the reduction of the Warsaw rising in 1944, in which it fired some 40 and 30 rounds respectively. The fate of this magnificent but completely extravagant weapon at the end of World War II remains unknown.

to produce greater stability as the projectile emerges from the muzzle, thereby enhancing accuracy at longer ranges; aerodynamically refined projectiles whose lower drag and greater stability also have an effect on range and accuracy; an auxiliary power unit that can operate a power loading system and also provide the equipment with the limited independent battlefield mobility required for rapid movement ('shoot-and-scoot') after a few rounds have been fired and before counter-fire can arrive; and considerably improved fire-control systems in which sensors provide data about ambient conditions (air pressure, air temperature, and wind speed and direction) and exact muzzle velocity for each round fired, so that the associated computer (with positional data provided by a land navigation system), can provide a high-quality solution to the fire-control problem and help to ensure that the target is hit as rapidly and effectively as possible for the expenditure of the minimum number of rounds.

Among the more important ammunition concepts to have emerged in recent years are rocket-assisted and base-bleed projectiles (the latter with a system to increase the pressure in the otherwise low-pressure area immediately to the rear of the projectile's flat base and so reduce drag) for considerably enhanced range without the need for a larger propellant charge.

Artillery equipments in service around the world, which provide striking evidence of the spread of artillery manufacturing capability, are detailed below by alphabetical order of the country of origin. The Austrian NORICUM GH N-45 155mm (6.1in) gun/howitzer is a towed gun/howitzer with a multi-baffle muzzle brake, a carriage of the split-trail type with four road wheels and two castors, a weight of 22,200lb (10,070kg), on-mounting elevation and traverse angles of –5 to +69 degrees and 30 and 40 degrees left and right respectively, a rate of fire of three rounds in 16 seconds (burst), two rounds per minute (normal) and seven rounds per minute (maximum), a range of 33,155yds (30,300m) with a normal round and 43,305yds (39,600m) with the base-bleed round, and a crew of six. Developed by Voerst-Alpine in Austria and marketed by NORICUM, this is an improved GC 45 (see below) with features designed to ease manufacture and to aid field reliability and handling; the most important modification is the optional addition of an auxiliary power unit (APU) for battlefield mobility. This APU

Ammunition Types for Tactical Flexibility

IN artillery with a calibre of more than 105mm (4.13in), it is standard for the ammunition to be of the separate-loading rather than fixed type, with the projectile loaded before one or more bagged propellant charges whose number is decided by the range required. This facilitates the task of the gun detachment in handling the ammunition and is more economical of propellant: in fixed ammunition, the propellant load is that required for maximum range and lower ranges are produced by alteration of the barrel's elevation, while with separate-loading ammunition the barrel elevation and propellant charge can be co-ordinated for maximum economy. The use of separate-loading ammunition also offers greater flexibility in the types of projectile that can be fired. In the standard NATO range for 155mm (6.1in) weapons, for instance, are the following projectiles produced by Talley Defense Systems Inc. that are in general matched by the products of other American and European companies: 110lb (49.91kg) M110 Chemical with an 11.68 or 9.68lb (5.3 or 4.39kg) load of Agent H or Agent HD; 103lb (46.7kg) M718 Anti-tank with nine M73 mines; 103lb M741 Anti-tank with nine M70 mines; 94.6lb (42.91kg) M107 HE with a 14.6 or 15.4lb (6.62 or 6.98kg) filling of TNT or Composition B; 95lb (43.09kg) M449 Anti-personnel with 60 M43 anti-personnel minelets; 102.6lb (46.54kg) M483A1 Anti-personnel/anti-vehicle with 64 M42 and 24 M46 dual-purpose minelets, 102.5lb (46.49kg) M692 Anti-personnel with 36 M67 minelets; 102.5lb M731 Anti-personnel with 36 M72 minelets; 103lb (46.72kg) M795 HE with a filling of cast TNT; 96lb (43.54kg) HE Rocket-assisted with 16 or 15lb (7.26 or 6.804kg) filling of Composition B or TNT; 102lb (46.26kg) M118 Illuminating with a 4.3lb (1.95kg) illuminant filling; 93.65lb (42.48kg) M485 Illuminating with a 5.95lb (2.7kg) illuminant filling; 93.1lb (42.22kg) M116 Smoke BE with a 25.84 or 17.88lb (11.72 or 8.11kg) filling of Agent HC or C; 97.9lb (44.4kg) M110 Smoke WP with 15.6lb (7.07kg) filling of white phosphorus; 96.75lb (43.88kg) M631 Tactical CS with a 14lb (6.35kg) filling of CS; and 98.9lb (44.86kg) M121 Chemical with a 15.87 or 6.48lb (7.2 or 2.94kg) filling of VX or GB.

is a 121hp (90kW) Porsche unit permitting a maximum speed of 18.6mph (30km/h) and a range of 93 miles (150km). The L/45 barrel has a semi-automatic breech with a pneumatically operated rammer, and optional features on the powered version are a powered traverse and elevation system, a six-round ammunition bracket, an ammunition-handling device and tracks to increase the traction of the wheels.

The Belgian SRC International GC 45 155mm (6.1in) gun/howitzer has an L.45 barrel with a multi-baffle muzzle brake, a split-trail carriage with four road wheels and two castors, a weight of 18,126lb (8,222kg), on-mounting elevation and traverse angles of –5 to +69 degrees and 80 degrees total respectively, a rate of fire of four rounds per minute (burst rate for 15 minutes) and two rounds per minute (normal), a range of 32,810yds (30,000m) with the normal round and 41,560yds (38,000m) with the base-bleed round, and a crew of eight. This weapon, designed in Canada and Belgium by the Space Research Corporation and PRB, is an advanced gun/howitzer designed to fire separate-loading ammunition (including all standard NATO 155mm/6.1in types) and fitted with an automatic breech and pneumatic rammer. The type is notable for the fact that its extended-range full-bore projectile reaches 32,810yds without rocket assistance, and this ERFB Mk 10 projectile weighs 100lb (45.4kg), contains 19.4lb (8.8kg) of HE and has a maximum muzzle velocity of 2,943ft (897m) per second.

The Chinese NORINCO Type 66 152mm (6in) gun/howitzer is a towed equipment with an L/34 barrel fitted with a single-baffle muzzle brake, a split-trail carriage with two road wheels and two castors, a weight of 12,610lb (5,720kg), on-mounting elevation and traverse arcs of –5 to +45 degrees and 58 degrees total respectively, a rate of fire of between six and eight rounds per minute under normal conditions, a maximum range of 18,845yds (17,230m), and a crew of 10 to 12. The Type 66 is the Chinese version of the Soviet D-20 equipment, and is notable for its light weight, comparatively large crew, and relatively short range for its calibre. The ordnance uses a variable six-charge propellant system, and can attain its maximum normal range with the 96lb (43.56kg) HE and smoke projectiles. The type can also fire an RAP of the same weight, range with this projectile being 23,930yds (21,880m) without any loss of accuracy.

The Chinese NORINCO Type 59-1 130mm (5.12in) gun is a towed equipment with an L/58.5 barrel fitted with a double-baffle muzzle brake, a split-trail carriage with two road wheels and two castors, a weight of 13,889lb (6,300kg),

The British 105mm (4.13in) Light Gun is typical of modern weapons optimised for maximum tactical versatility through the combination of an advanced ordnance and sight system, with a carriage that is sturdy enough for all tactical purposes but light enough for easy carriage by tactical transports of the fixed- and rotary-wing types.

on-mounting elevation and traverse angles of –2.5 to +45 degrees and 58 degrees total respectively, a rate of fire of between eight and 10 rounds per minute under normal conditions, a range of 30,065yds (27,490m) with the normal round, 34,995yds (32,000m) with the base-bleed round and 37,575yds (34,260m) with the rocket-assisted projectile, and a crew of between eight and 10. The Type 59 is the Chinese copy of the Soviet M-46 equipment. The Type 59-1 variant is a simple combination of the Type 59 with features of the Type 60 (Chinese copy of the Soviet D-74) to produce an equipment that is better disposed than the Type 59. The Type 59-1 uses a scaled-up version of the Type 60's muzzle brake, recoil system and breech on a carriage with a number of Type 60 features. In combination with a lighter shield, this produces an equipment that is more manoeuvrable and has the additional advantage of not requiring the Type 59's two-wheel limber; the Type 59-1 fires a 73.6lb (33.4kg) HE projectile with a muzzle velocity of 3,051ft (930m) per minute, an RAP of the same weight, a 71.45lb (32.4kg) RAP, and an illuminating projectile.

The Finnish Tampella M-60 122mm (4.8in) field gun is a towed equipment with an L/53 barrel fitted with a single-baffle muzzle brake, a split-trail carriage with four road wheels, a weight of 18,739lb (8,500kg), on-mounting elevation and traverse angles of –5 to +50 degrees and 90 degrees total respectively, a rate of fire of four rounds per minute, a range of 27,340yds (25,000m), and a crew of eight. Entering service in 1964, the M-60 is a powerful equipment with a semi-automatic breech and firing separate-loading ammunition including a 55.1lb HE projectile with a muzzle velocity of 3,117ft (950m) per second. The four-wheel bogie can be powered hydraulically from the towing vehicle for improved cross-country mobility.

The French GIAT TR 155mm (6.1in) gun is a towed equipment with an L/40 barrel fitted with a double-baffle muzzle brake, a split-trail carriage with two road wheels, a weight of about 23,479lb (10,650kg), on-mounting elevation and traverse angles of –5 to +66 and 27 and 38 degrees left and right respectively, a rate of fire of three rounds in 18 seconds with a cold barrel, six rounds per minute for 2 minutes and two rounds per minute under normal conditions, a range of 26,245yds (24,000m) with a hollow-base projectile and 36,090yds (33,000m) with an RAP, and a crew of eight. Entering production in 1984, the TR is a modern equipment designed for the support of motorised divisions. A hydraulically powered rammer is standard to reduce crew fatigue, and helps the equipment to generate a high initial rate of fire with its standard French separate-loading ammunition: types include HE with a projectile weight of 95.35lb (43.25kg) and a muzzle velocity of 2,723ft per second for a range of 26,245yds, HE RAP with a projectile weight of 95.9lb (43.5kg) and a muzzle velocity of 2,723f per second for a range of 36,090yds, anti-tank mine-launching with a projectile weight of 101.4lb (46kg) and a load of six 1.2lb (0.55kg) mines, smoke and illuminating. The TR can also fire the US M107 round and the ammunition of the FH-70 series, and a measure of battlefield mobility is provided by the 39hp (29kW) auxiliary power unit, which offers a road speed of 5mph (8km/h).

The German, Italian and British Rheinmetall/OTO Melara/Vickers FH-70 155mm (6.1in) field howitzer is typical of the modern practice of international collaboration to reduce the development and production costs of expensive primary equipment, and is a towed equipment with an L/38.85 barrel fitted with a single-baffle muzzle brake, a split-trail carriage with an auxiliary power unit, two road wheels and two castors, a weight of 20,503lb (9,300kg), on-mounting elevation and traverse angles of –5 to +70 and 56 degrees total respectively, a rate of fire of three rounds in eight seconds with the optional flick loader, three rounds in 13 seconds (bursts), six rounds per

minute (normal) and two rounds per minute (sustained fire), a range of 26,245yds with the standard projectile and 32,810yds with the RAP, and a crew of eight. Developed jointly by West Germany, Italy and the UK in the late 1960s and entering service from 1978, the FH-70 is an advanced field howitzer firing its own special separate-loading ammunition as well as standard NATO types and the Copperhead cannon-launched guided projectile. The type uses a semi-automatic breech and loader for reduced crew fatigue and high rates of fire, with a flick loader optional for even higher rates, while the addition of a Volkswagen petrol-engined auxiliary power unit provides power for getting the equipment into and out of action, and also gives good battlefield mobility at speeds of up to 10mph (16km/h), gradients of 34% and a fording depth of 0.75m (2.5ft). Included in the ammunition types are the 95.9lb FRAG-HE projectile with 24.9lb (11.3kg) of HE, HE RAP, smoke and illuminating. The use of an eight-charge propellant system allows muzzle velocities of between 700 and 2,715ft (213 and 827m) per second. The FH-70R is an improved model developed as a private venture by Rheinmetall. This has an L/46 barrel, making possible ranges of 32,810yds with the standard projectile and 39,370yds (36,000m) with a base-bleed projectile. Rheinmetall is also developing combustible charge containers for this weapon and other 155mm types.

The Israeli Soltam Model 839P 155mm (6.1in) gun/howitzer is a towed equipment with an L/43 barrel fitted with a single-baffle muzzle brake, a split-trail carriage with an auxiliary power unit, four road wheels and two castors, a weight of 23,920lb (10,850kg), on-mounting elevation and traverse angles of –3 to +70 degrees and 78 degrees total respectively, a rate of fire of four rounds per minute (short periods) and two rounds per minute (sustained fire), a range of 25,700yds (23,500m), and a crew of eight. This equipment, which is a development of the same company's M-71 weapon, is produced in two variants as the Model 839P and the Model 845P. The Model 839P entered service in 1984 and uses the same ordnance on a revised carriage fitted with an 80hp (60kW) Deutz diesel-engined auxiliary power unit for a road speed of 10.6mph (17km/h), has a range of 43.5 miles (70km) and a gradient capability of 34%, as well as power for trail-spreading/opening, wheel lifting/lowering and firing platform lowering/lifting. A pneumatically operated rammer eases crew fatigue and increases rate of fire, and the ordnance fires separate-loading ammunition of various types including the 95.9lb FRAG-HE with 18.74lb/8.5kg of HE and the HE RAP with 9.9lb/4.5kg of HE. Entering service in 1985, the Model 845P is a version of the Model 839P with an L/45 barrel and a range of 31,170yds (28,500m) with a 'special projectile'.

The Israeli Soltam M-71 155mm (6.1in) gun/howitzer is a towed equipment with an L/39 barrel fitted with a single-baffle muzzle brake, a split-trail carriage with four road wheels, a weight of 20,282lb (9,200kg), on-mounting elevation and traverse angles of –3 to +54 degrees and 84 degrees total respectively, a rate of fire of four rounds per minute (short periods) and two rounds per minute (sustained fire), a range of 25,700yds, and a crew of eight. The M-71 is a development of the same company's M-68 equipment with a longer ordnance and a compressed-air rammer for rapid reloading at all angles of elevation. The ammunition types used with the M-71 are those detailed for the M-68.

The Israeli Soltam M-68 155mm (6.1in) gun/howitzer is a towed equipment with an L/33 barrel fitted with a single-baffle muzzle brake, a split-trail carriage with four road wheels, a weight of 20,944lb (9,500kg) in travelling order and 18,739lb (8,500kg) in firing position, on-mounting elevation and traverse angles of –5 to +52 degrees and 90 degrees total respectively, a rate of fire of four rounds per minute (short periods) and two

One of the most advanced items of conventional towed artillery in current service, the 155mm (6.1in) FH-70 was developed jointly by British, German and Italian interests, and is a highly capable equipment offering considerable range and accuracy.

rounds per minute (sustained fire), a range of 22,965yds (21,000m) with NATO ammunition and 25,700yds with Tampella ammunition, and a crew of eight. The M-68 is the baseline variant of Israel's important 155mm gun/howitzer family, and combines an Israeli ordnance on a locally developed adaptation of the carriage of the Finnish M-60. Development of the M-68 was undertaken in the 1960s, final trials being completed in 1968 for the equipment to enter service in 1970. The ordnance fires all standard NATO projectiles of this calibre, the 96.3lb (43.7kg) HE projectile leaving the muzzle at 2,379ft (725m) per second to attain a range of 22,965yds, although the weapon can also use the more capable range of ammunition developed by Tampella, using a nine-charge propellant system to attain a maximum range of 25,700yds.

The South African Armscor G5 155mm gun/howitzer is a towed equipment with an L/45 barrel fitted with a single-baffle muzzle brake, a split-trail carriage with an auxiliary power unit, four road wheels and two castors, a weight of 29,762lb (13,510kg), on-mounting elevation and traverse angles of respectively –3 to +75 degrees and 84 degrees total up to +15 degrees of elevation to 65 degrees total above 15 degrees of elevation, a rate of fire of three rounds per minute (15-minute period) and two rounds per minute (normal), a range of 32,810yds with standard ammunition and 41,010yds (37,500m) with HE base-bleed ammunition, and a crew of eight. The G5 is an extremely potent piece of equipment, and was developed from

Although most modern armies have opted for the logistic simplicity of using mainly the 155mm (6.1in) calibre in weapons that can be used in the direct- and indirect-fire roles, the USA still has small numbers of larger-calibre weapons in service. These are typified here by the 175mm (6.89in) M107 self-propelled gun, which was used in Vietnam for the long-range bombardment of targets such as Viet Cong build-up areas and suspected supply dumps.

1975 on the basis of the GC 45, although the process altered virtually every feature of the Canadian/Belgian weapon. The weapon entered South African service in 1983 and has proved very successful in terms of range, accuracy and cross-country mobility. Battlefield capabilities are considerably aided by the installation of a 68hp (51kW) Magirus-Deutz diesel-engined auxiliary power unit for hydraulic functions such as lowering/raising the firing platform and castors, and for opening/closing the trails, while crew fatigue is reduced by the provision of a pneumatically operated rammer. A three-charge propellant system is used for muzzle velocities of between 820 and 2,943ft (250 and 897m) per second, and the projectile types are 100.3lb (45.5kg) HE, 103.6lb (47kg) base-bleed HE, smoke, illuminating, white phosphorus and cargo-carrying rounds.

The Swedish Bofors FH-77A 155mm (6.1in) field howitzer is a towed equipment with an L/38 barrel fitted with a 'pepperpot' muzzle brake, a split-trail carriage with an auxiliary power unit, two road wheels and two castors, a weight of 25,353lb (11,500kg), on-mounting elevation and traverse angles of respectively –3 to +50 degrees and 50 degrees total up to +5 degrees of elevation to 60 degrees total above 5 degrees of elevation, a rate of fire of three rounds in 6–8 seconds or six rounds in 20–25 seconds (bursts) and six rounds every other minute (20-minute period), a range of 24,060yds (22,000m), and a crew of six. The FH-77A entered production in 1975, and is a highly capable equipment although only at great cost and considerable size. One of the main features of the equipment is its use of a Volvo B20 auxiliary power unit for a hydraulic system that drives the road wheels and castors, providing good battlefield mobility (at a maximum speed of 5mph/8km/h) and competent into/out of action times. Elevation and traverse are also hydraulically powered, and a powered rammer is used in conjunction with a crane-supplied loading table (the crane delivering three projectiles at a time) and semi-automatic breech for very high burst rates of fire. The FH-77A fires particularly potent separate-loading ammunition, the HE projectile weighing 93lb (42.2kg). The weapon uses a six-charge propellant system offering muzzle velocities between 1,017 and 2,539ft (310 and 774m) per second with projectiles that include HE, base-bleed HE, smoke and illuminating. The FH-77B is the export version of the FH-77A with a longer L/39 barrel, a screw rather than vertical sliding wedge breech mechanism, a fully automatic ammunition-handling system, elevation to +70 degrees, and improvements to cross-country mobility (including power take-off from the tractor to provide full 8x8 drive for the tractor/ordnance combination). The weight is increased to 26,235lb (11,900kg), and a bagged rather than cartridge charge propellant system is used. The standard range of the FH-77B is 26,245yds (24,000m) rising to 32,810yds with an extended-range full-bore round. The FH-77B can also be fitted with the Ferranti FIN 1150 gyrostabilised land navigation system to permit autonomous positioning of the equipment: trials have confirmed the utility of such a system for 'shoot-and-scoot' tactics, one equipment (with a crew of four men) in a period of 5 minutes 10 seconds coming into action, firing four rounds, moving 55yds (50m) and firing another three rounds.

The Soviet (now Russian) S-23 180mm (7.09in) gun is a towed equipment with an L/48.9 barrel fitted with a 'pepperpot' muzzle brake, a split-trail carriage with four road wheels and a two-wheel limber, a weight of 47,288lb (21,450kg), on-mounting elevation and traverse angles of –2 to +50 degrees and 44 degrees total respectively, a rate of fire of one round per minute (bursts) and one round per two minutes (sustained fire), a range of 33,245yds (30,400m) with normal ammunition and 47,900yds (43,800m) with an RAP, and a crew of 16. Originally thought by Western analysts to be a 203mm (8in) weapon, the S-23 was at first known in US terminology as the M1955 and

The air portability of modern artillery is revealed here by the carriage of a 105mm (4.13in) Light Gun by an Aérospatiale SA 330 Puma medium-lift helicopter.

originated as a naval weapon in the early 1950s. To facilitate towed transport, the ordnance can be withdrawn from battery and the ends of the trails supported on a two-wheel limber. The type fires separate-loading ammunition with variable bag charges, and the projectiles include a 185.4lb (84.09kg) HE type fired at a muzzle velocity of 2,592ft (790m) per second, an HE RAP type fired at a muzzle velocity of 2,789ft (850m) per second, a 215.4lb (97.7kg) concrete-piercing type, and a nuclear type with a yield of 0.2 kilotons.

The Soviet (now Russian) 2A36 152mm (6in) field gun is a towed equipment with a barrel of unknown length fitted with a multi-baffle muzzle brake, a split-trail carriage with four road wheels, a weight of about 19,400lb (8,800kg), on-mounting elevation and traverse angles of –2 to +57 degrees and 25 degrees left and right respectively, a rate of fire of five or six rounds per minute, a range of 29,530yds (27,000m) with the standard projectile and 40,465yds (37,000m) with an RAP, and a crew of 10. The 2A46 is generally known in the West as the M1976, which is its designation in the US system of terminology. This equipment began to enter service in 1981 and is apparently the modern replacement for the 130mm (5.12in) M-46 gun in the counter-battery role with army-level artillery divisions and brigades. The ordnance can fire HE, RAP, HEAT, chemical and nuclear projectiles of the separate-loading type, and the 101.4lb (46kg) HE fragmentation projectile is fired at a muzzle velocity of 2,625ft (800m) per second.

The Soviet (now Russian) D-20 152mm (6in) gun/howitzer is a towed equipment with an L/37 barrel fitted with a double-baffle muzzle brake, a split-trail carriage with two road wheels and two castors, a weight of 12,556lb (5,700kg) in travelling order and 12,456lb (5,650kg) in firing position, on-mounting elevation and traverse angles of –5 to +63 degrees and 58 degrees total respectively, a rate of fire of five or six rounds per minute, a range of 19,030yds (17,400m) with a standard projectile and 26,245yds (24,000m) with an RAP, and a crew of 10. Developed after World War II for a service debut in the early 1950s, the D-20 was initially called the M1955 in the West and was designed as successor to the ML-20. The recoil system and carriage are identical to those of the D-74 field gun although supporting a shorter and considerably fatter ordnance. The equipment fires separate-loading case ammunition with several projectiles, including a 95.9lb (43.51kg) HE-FRAG type at a muzzle velocity of 2,149ft (655m) per second, an HE RAP type to a maximum range of 26,245yds, a 107.5lb (48.78kg) AP-T type at a muzzle velocity of 1,969ft (600m) per second to penetrate 124mm (4.88in) of armour at 1,095yds (1,000m), a HEAT type, a concrete-piercing type, a smoke type, an illuminating type, a chemical type and a nuclear type with a yield of 0.2 kilotons. The M84 is the Yugoslav-made version of the D-20. This uses the same carriage as the D-20 but possesses a number of improved features including a longer barrel and two hydraulic pumps used to locate the weapon on its circular firing platform and raise the wheels clear of the ground; maximum rate of fire is six rounds per minute, and the Yugoslav ordnance can fire the same ammunition as the Soviet weapon, including the OF-540 HE-FRAG projectile, but can also fire the new Yugoslav M84 HE projectile: this is fired with a muzzle velocity of 2,657ft (810m) per second to attain a maximum range of 26,245yds. Also available are an illuminating projectile and the new High Explosive/Improved Conventional Munition (HE/ICM), the latter carrying 63 KB-2 bomblets to a range of 24,605yds (22,500m): each of these top-attack anti-armour bomblets weighs 0.55lb (0.25kg). The Type 66 is the Chinese-made copy of the D-20.

The nature of the modern 155mm (6.1in) howitzer is exemplified by this American prototype weapon. The main picture shows the moment of firing, the projectile emerging from the muzzle whose brake is just capturing and diverting part of the propellant gases to reduce the recoil. Note (left) the small radar used to capture the exact velocity of the departing projectile.

The Soviet (now Russian) M-46 130mm (5.12in) field gun is a towed equipment with an L/55 barrel fitted with a 'pepperpot' muzzle brake, a split-trail carriage with two road wheels and a two-wheel limber, a weight of 18,629lb (8,450kg) in travelling order and 16,975lb (7,700kg) in firing position, on-mounting elevation and traverse angles of –2.5 to +45 degrees and 50 degrees total respectively, a rate of fire of five or six rounds per minute, a range of 29,690yds (27,150m), and a crew of nine. Introduced in the early 1950s as successor to the A-19 (M1931/37) gun, the M-46 has its ordnance pulled right back out of battery for towed transport. The type's ordnance is essentially similar to 130mm guns used in warships of the Soviet navy, and fires separate-loading case-type ammunition with projectiles such as a 73.6lb (33.4kg) HE-FRAG type fired at a muzzle velocity of 3,445ft (1,050m) per second and an APC-T type fired at the same muzzle velocity to penetrate 230mm (9.06in) of armour at a range of 1,095yds as well as HE RAP, smoke and illuminating types.

The Soviet (now Russian) D-74 122mm (4.8in) field gun is a towed equipment with an L/47 barrel fitted with a double-baffle muzzle brake, a split-trail carriage with two road wheels and two castors, a weight of 12,235lb (5,550kg) in travelling order and 12,125lb (5,500kg) in firing position, on-mounting elevation and traverse angles of –5 to +45 degrees and 58 degrees total respectively, a rate of fire of six or seven rounds per minute, a range of 26,245yds, and a crew of 10. Designed in the late 1940s as a possible successor to the A-19 (M1931/37) gun, the D-74 was at first known in the West as the M1955 but not adopted by the Soviet army, which instead accepted the 130mm M-46. The D-74 uses the same carriage as the D-20 152mm gun/howitzer, and was widely produced for export. The type is

Another photograph of the same development weapon for the M198 howitzer shows the compact design but sturdy construction.

Above and below: Keys to modern artillery design include comparatively small wheels, a light but very rigid carriage and cradle allowing the ordnance to be reversed for towing, an effective muzzle brake (often including the towing eye in its lower edge), a stable firing platform created by the trail legs and/or outrigger legs, and often the ability to move short distances on the battlefield as a result of the incorporation of an auxiliary power unit.

installed on a circular firing platform for operation, and fires separate-loading case-type ammunition: among the projectiles available are a 60.2lb (27.3kg) HE-FRAG type fired at a muzzle velocity of 2,904ft (885m) per second and a 55.1lb (25kg) APC-T type fired at the same muzzle velocity to penetrate 185mm (7.28in) of armour at a range of 1,095yds as well as chemical, illuminating and smoke types. The Type 60 is the Chinese-made copy of the D-74.

The Soviet (now Russian) D-30 122mm (4.8in) howitzer is a towed equipment with an L/35.5 barrel fitted with a multi-baffle muzzle brake, a three-leg split-trail carriage with two road wheels, a weight of 7,077lb (3,210kg) in travelling order and 6,944lb (3,150kg) in firing position, on-mounting elevation and traverse angles of –7 to +70 degrees and 360 degrees respectively, a rate of fire of seven or eight rounds per minute, a range of 16,840yds (15,400m) with standard ammunition and 23,950yds (21,900m) with an RAP, and a crew of seven. Entering service in the early 1960s as successor to the M-30, the D-30 offers useful advantages such as 360-degree traverse (on its three-leg firing platform) and greater range. The weapon is towed by its muzzle and fires separate-loading case-type ammunition; among the projectiles available are a 47.97lb (21.76kg) HE-FRAG type fired at a muzzle velocity of 2,264ft (690m) per second and a 47.7lb (21.63kg) HEAT-FS type fired at a muzzle velocity of 2,428ft (740m) per second to penetrate 460mm (18.1in) of armour at any range, as well as HE RAP, chemical, illuminating and smoke types. The Type 83 is the Chinese-made version of the D-30.

The British L118A1 105mm (4.13in) Light Gun is a towed equipment with an L/29.2 barrel fitted with a double-baffle muzzle brake, a split-trail carriage with two road wheels, a weight of 4,100lb (1,860kg), on-mounting elevation and traverse angles of –5.5 to +70 degrees and 11 degrees total (increasing to 360 degrees on the firing platform) respectively, a rate of fire of eight rounds in 60 seconds (burst), six rounds per minute (three-minute period) and three rounds per minute (sustained fire), a range of 18,800yds (17,190m) and a crew of six. Introduced in 1974, the L118A1 Light Gun is the basic electrically fired British version of the Light Gun and is a thoroughly modern piece of equipment designed to fulfil the pack howitzer and gun roles while being air-portable under medium-lift helicopters. The ordnance fires semi-fixed ammunition with a seven-charge propellant system offering ranges between 2,750 and 18,800yds (2,515 and 17,190m). The projectile types available are 35.5lb (16.1kg) HE, 23.1lb (10.49kg) HESH, illuminating and three smoke varieties. The L118F1 Hamel is the version of the L118A1 built under licence in Australia for the Australian and New Zealand armies.

The L119A1 Hamel is the version developed for the US M1 ammunition series with different rifling, a single-baffle muzzle brake, percussion firing and a maximum range of 12,000yds (10,975m): the type is used by Australia and New Zealand as a training weapon for the L118F1, using existing stocks of US-supplied ammunition, and its shorter range renders it more appropriate for operational training in battle areas. The L127A1 is the version developed for Switzerland with different rifling, a double-baffle muzzle brake and percussion firing.

The American M198 155mm (6.1in) howitzer is a towed equipment with an L/39.3 barrel fitted with a double-baffle muzzle brake, a split-trail carriage with two road wheels, a weight of 15,790lb (7,162kg), on-mounting elevation and traverse angles of –5 to +72 degrees and 45 degrees total respectively, a rate of fire of four rounds per minute, a range of 19,850yds (18,150m) with the HE grenade-launching projectile and 32,800yds (29,995m) with the HE RAP, and a crew of 11. The M198 was designed as successor to the M114 series and began to enter US service in 1978. The type is designed to fire the full range of standard NATO separate-loading ammunition, and projectiles that can be used are two types of HE mine-launcher each weighing 102.5lb (46.5kg) and carrying 36 anti-personnel mines, two types of HE grenade-launcher (a 102.57lb/46.52kg type with 88 dual-purpose grenades and a 95lb/43.09kg type with 60 anti-personnel grenades), a 96lb (43.54kg) HE RAP type fired at a muzzle velocity of 2,710ft (826m) per second, two types of HE mine-launcher each weighing 103lb (46.72kg) with nine anti-tank mines, the Copperhead laser-guided anti-tank projectile, three chemical/gas types, two illuminating types, two smoke types and the M454 nuclear type with a 0.1-kiloton W48 warhead (to have been replaced by the W82 enhanced-radiation 'neutron' warhead).

Modern towed artillery is designed for the long-range delivery of several accurately aimed projectiles within as short a space of time as possible, and then departure from the firing position before counter-fire can arrive and destroy the equipment.

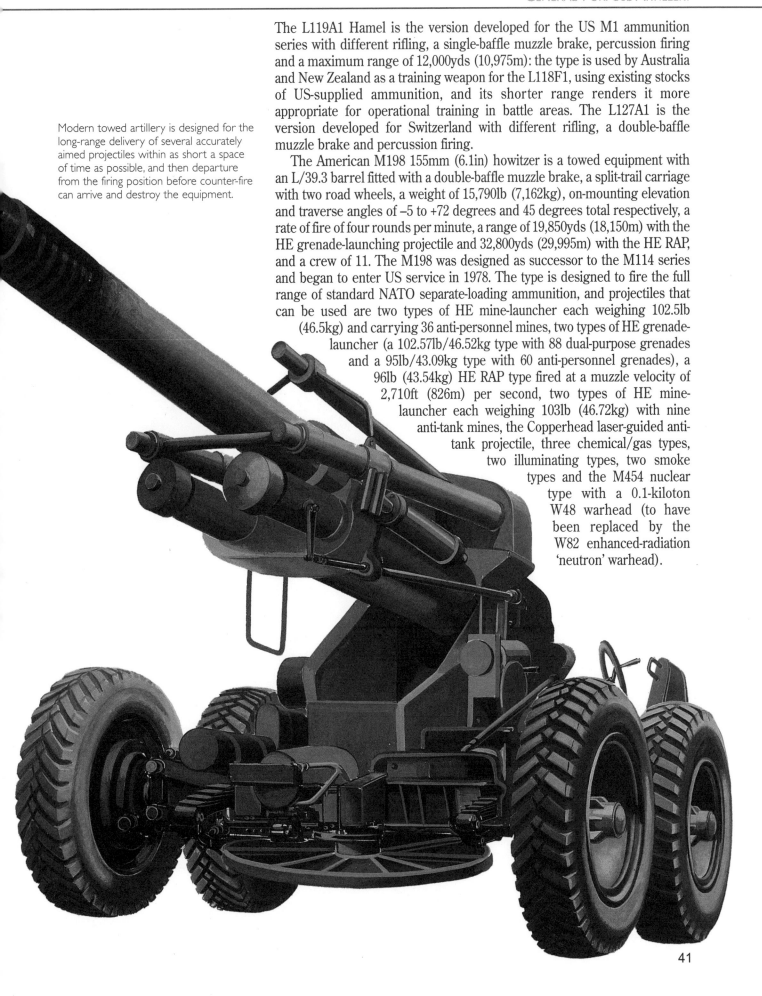

Special-Purpose Artillery

FIELD artillery of the light, medium and heavy types was designed for multi-purpose tactical use, but under certain circumstances could also be fired in more specialised roles such as the anti-tank and, to a lesser extent, anti-aircraft tasks. The Soviets in particular were avid exponents of the theory that every piece of artillery should be used for the anti-tank role when required, and therefore designed an anti-tank round for use with virtually every calibre of gun in the light, medium and heavy ranges. This was not allowed to disguise the fact that the anti-tank and anti-aircraft roles were best served by more specialised weapons, however, as these tasks required not only particular types of projectile but also a number of particular features in the guns themselves.

Both anti-tank and anti-aircraft guns were used in World War I, but these were not so much specialised weapons as lighter pieces of field artillery, either firing special ammunition, or being installed on dedicated mountings (often on the back of trucks for greater tactical mobility), allowing the guns to be elevated to a far higher angle than had been possible in the guns' original surface-to-surface role.

As the threat of the tank and the warplane increased during the 1920s and 1930s, specialised weapons (mostly of indigenous manufacture) began to appear on the equipment strengths of most European nations as well as the USA and Japan. The emphasis in this new type of specialised weapon was a high muzzle velocity as this was required by both the anti-tank gun and the aircraft gun: the former needed the velocity for the flattest and therefore most easily aimed fire with the maximum possible kinetic energy in the short-range task of penetrating armour with a solid shot, while the latter required velocity for the delivery of an explosive-filled shell to the desired altitude in the shortest possible time and with the straightest possible trajectory.

As the international situation began to decline in the 1930s with the rise of aggressive intention displayed by Germany, Italy and Japan, new generations of better protected tanks and faster- and higher-flying aircraft began to enter service, and this placed fresh emphasis on the need for high muzzle velocities for both anti-tank guns and anti-aircraft guns.

In World War II, the countries that developed, procured and used the most effective anti-tank guns were Germany, the UK, the USA and the USSR, whose primary weapons of this type are detailed below by country and in ascending order of calibre.

The smallest of the German weapons was the 28mm schwere Panzerbüchse (sPzB) 41 that entered service in 1941 as the world's first operational expression of the Gerlich-designed 'taper bore' concept. The sPzB 41 therefore fired a 28mm round whose 4.5oz (0.1305kg) solid projectile was fitted with collapsing annular skirts that allowed it to decrease in diameter as it was pushed up the tapered barrel to emerge from the 20mm muzzle with the very high velocity of 4,599ft (1,402m) per second for

Experience in World War II soon revealed what the prophets of armoured warfare had foretold, namely that armoured formations should be accompanied by self-propelled artillery as towed equipment could not keep pace with it. One of the best such equipments developed in World War II by the Americans was the Howitzer Motor Carriage M7, known to the British as 'the Priest' because of its 'pulpit' for the defensive machine gun: this was based on the chassis and lower hull of the M3 medium tank with a raised cupola carrying the 105mm (4.13in) M101 howitzer.

the ability to penetrate 56mm (2.2in) of armour at a range of 440yds (402m) at an impact angle of 30 degrees. The ordnance was installed in a light two-wheeled carriage of the split-trail type, had on-mounting elevation and traverse angles of -5 to +45 degrees and 90 degrees (reducing to 30 degrees at maximum elevation) total respectively, and a weight of 505lb (229kg). The sPzB 41 was an effective weapon offering good armour-penetration qualities for its weight, but the ordnance was difficult and therefore expensive to manufacture, and as Germany's supplies of strategic raw materials dwindled later in the war, the manufacture of the weapon was discontinued because of the difficulties of supplying its ammunition, which was based on a shot with a small-diameter tungsten core whose density and strength offered the best possible armour-penetration capability.

The smallest 'conventional' anti-tank gun used by the Germans was a Rheinmetall production, the 37mm Panzerabwehrkanone (PaK) 35/36. This was a simple weapon based on a two-wheeled light carriage of the split-trail type with a shield, and was developed from 1933 for a service debut during 1936 in the Spanish Civil War (1936-39). The L/45 barrel fired the 1.5lb (0.68kg) solid shot at a muzzle velocity of 2,499ft (762m) per second to penetrate 38mm (1.5in) of armour at a range of 440yds at an impact angle of 30 degrees: by 1940 the obsolescence of the weapon was realised in face of the latest British and French tanks, and the original ammunition was replaced by the AP40 type with a high-density tungsten core, and this 12.5oz (0.354kg) projectile was fired at a muzzle velocity of 3,378ft (1,030m) per second to penetrate 49mm (1.93in) of armour at a range of 440yds at an impact angle of 30 degrees. The complete equipment, of which more than 15,000 had been completed by 1941 for export as well as German use, weighed 952lb (432kg) in travelling order and 723lb (328kg) in firing position, and its on-mounting elevation and traverse angles were -8 to +25 degrees and 60 degrees total respectively. The AP40 shot was later supplemented by the Stielgranate spigot grenade in an effort to retain an operational effectiveness in the face of Allied tanks with thicker and better

Low and light, the British 6pdr anti-tank gun was a 57mm weapon that offered good capabilities within the limitation of its calibre but was already on the verge of obsolescence even as it entered service.

angled protective armour, but by 1943 the PaK 35/36 was obsolete even though it soldiered on to the end of the war in a number of second-line units. As well as being exported, the weapon was licensed for foreign production, and several other weapons were modelled closely on the German original, a good example being the American 37mm M3 weapon.

The 42mm leichte Panzerabwehrkanone 41 that entered service in 1941 was another taper-bore weapon based on a development of the PaK 35/36's carriage with sprung suspension and a spaced shield for improved protection against small-arms and shell fragments. The complete equipment weighed 992lb (450kg) and possessed on-mounting elevation and traverse angles of -8 to +25 degrees and 41 degrees total respectively, and the barrel tapered from 40.5mm at the breech to 29.4mm at the muzzle, resulting in the firing of the 11.75oz (0.336kg) shot at a muzzle velocity of 4,149ft (1,265m) per second to penetrate 72mm (2.84in) of armour at a range of 545yds (498m) at an impact angle of 30 degrees. This lightweight weapon was intended for use by the German air force's parachute arm, but supplies of tungsten for the core of the solid projectile were so limited that production was ended in 1942 after the delivery of only a small number of equipments.

The 50mm PaK 38 was designed by Rheinmetall from 1938 as successor to the PaK 35/36 with considerably improved armour-penetration capability, and entered service in the later part of 1940 as an excellent type that was later provided with improved ammunition that allowed it to remain in service up to the end of World War II. The PaK 38 was based on a two-wheel carriage of the split-trail type with a shield, the complete equipment weighed 2,174lb (986kg), and the on-mounting elevation and traverse angles were -8 to +27 degrees and 65 degrees total respectively. The L/60 barrel was fitted with a double-baffle muzzle brake and fired the 4.96lb (2.25kg) standard shot to penetrate 61mm (2.4in) of armour at a range of 545yds at an impact angle of 30 degrees, but the improved tungsten-cored 2.15lb (0.97kg) AP40 projectile left the muzzle with a velocity of 3,937ft (1,200m) per second to penetrate 86mm (3.39in) of armour at a range of 545yds at an impact angle of 30 degrees. The weight of the equipment was usefully reduced by the use of light alloys in place of steel for certain parts of the carriage and trail, and handling was facilitated by the use of a small castor inserted under the trails in the joined position.

The only weapon wholly designed in Japan for the anti-tank gun role, the 47mm Anti-Tank Gun Type 1 appeared in 1941, and although of moderately advanced design and appearance, was somewhat lacking in performance by comparison with other nations' towed anti-tank guns. The type had an L/54 barrel, weighed 1,660lb (753kg), possessed an elevation arc of between −11 and +19 degrees as well as a traverse of 30 degrees left and right of the centreline, and fired its 3.08lb (1.4kg) shot at a muzzle velocity of 2,701ft (825m) per second to penetrate 2in (50mm) of armour at 545yds (500m) at an angle of 30 degrees.

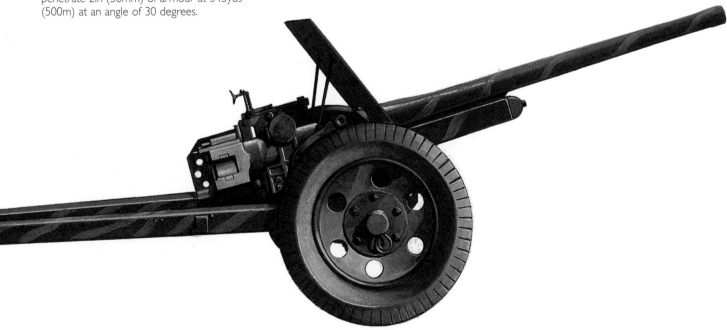

The Italian Semovente M.41M da 90/53 was produced only in small numbers, but was an impressive equipment that added the 90mm (3.54in) anti-aircraft gun in a low-angle traversing and shielded mounting on the hull of the M.14/41 medium tank chassis. The result was a powerful self-propelled anti-tank weapon.

Another Rheinmetall design, the PaK 40 was developed from 1939 in response to a German army requirement for a weapon offering significantly better armour-penetration capabilities than the PaK 38. The resulting weapon entered service in the later part of 1941 as a scaled-up version of the PaK 38, and was later provided with improved ammunition that allowed it to remain in service up to the end of World War II. The PaK 40 was based on a two-wheel carriage of the split-trail type with a shield (in this instance made of straight rather than curved sections of steel plate to simplify the production process), the complete equipment weighed 3,307lb (1,500kg), and the on-mounting elevation and traverse angles were –5 to +22 degrees and 65 degrees total respectively. The L/46 barrel was fitted with a double-baffle muzzle brake and fired the 15lb (6.8kg) standard shot to penetrate 106mm (4.17in) of armour at a range of 545yds at an impact angle of 30 degrees, but the improved tungsten-cored 7lb (3.2kg) AP40 projectile left the muzzle with a velocity of 3,068ft (935m) per second to penetrate 115mm (4.53in) of armour at a range of 545yds at an impact angle of 30 degrees.

Although the PaK 38 and PaK 40 offered a useful capability against the majority of Soviet tanks in the first phases of Germany's invasion of the USSR from June 1941, the rapid emergence of tanks such as the T-34 and KV series, which were soon available to the Soviets in very substantial numbers, presented the Germans with an increasingly acute problem in armour penetration with the tungsten-cored AP40 type of projectile. The Germans were therefore steadily reduced from the later part of 1942 to the ambush type of engagement in which the less well protected flanks and rear of the Soviet's tanks could be attacked as they passed the German anti-tank gun positions. The German army had anticipated this eventuality, although somewhat belatedly, and the result was the devastating 88mm (3.465in) PaK 43 that was in overall terms the finest anti-tank gun of World War II. Designed by Krupp, the PaK 43 was based on a four-wheel carriage of the four-trail type with a wide and well-sloped shield, the complete equipment weighed 11,023lb (5,000kg), and the on-mounting elevation and traverse angles were –8 to +40 degrees and 60 degrees total respectively. The L/71 barrel was fitted with a double-baffle muzzle brake and fired the 16.1lb

(7.3kg) standard shot with a muzzle velocity of 3,708ft (1,130m) per second to penetrate 226mm (8.9in) of armour at a range of 545yds at an impact angle of 30 degrees. In firing position the trails were opened out into a large cruciform and then lowered to the ground with the wheels removed, to create a firing platform of great stability and weapon traverse of 360 degrees, and the weapon was also a general-purpose utility being provided with a 30.8lb (13.97kg) HE shell. The overall effect of this powerful weapon, whose carriage was based on that of the 88mm anti-aircraft gun and was generally operated in the dug-in position, was its considerable armour-penetration capability at long range: this meant that the T-34 and KV tanks could be engaged frontally at long range in the shorter term, and in the longer term provided the Germans with a weapon that could tackle the IS series of tanks, which appeared in 1944, at short ranges.

Such was the success of the PaK 43 that demand for this potent weapon soon outstripped supply, especially as the Krupp factories were among the German industrial targets attacked most frequently by British bombers. In fact, it was production of the carriage that fell behind that of the ordnance, and so the ordnance was adapted to a revised version of the carriage of the 105mm leFH 18 howitzer to create the 88mm PaK 43/41. The PaK 43/41 was without doubt a less elegant weapon than the PaK 43, but possessed all the original ordnance's tank-killing capabilities.

The United Kingdom used three main types of anti-tank gun in World War II, in the form of 2pdr, 6pdr and 17pdr weapons whose weight of shot is a telling indication of the thickness of protective armour that had to be penetrated during the war's six-year course.

The Ordnance, QF, 2pdr was developed in response to an official requirement issued in 1934, and entered service in 1938 as a simple yet effective weapon based on a two-wheel carriage of the split-trail type with

A fairly potent anti-aircraft gun mounting of the self-propelled type for the period in the middle of World War II, the mittlerer Zugkraftwagen 8t mit 3,7cm FlaK 36, otherwise known as the SdKfz 7/2, combined the 3.7cm FlaK 36 anti-aircraft gun with the SdKfz 7 semi-tracked vehicle to provide a good measure of road performance and cross-country capability.

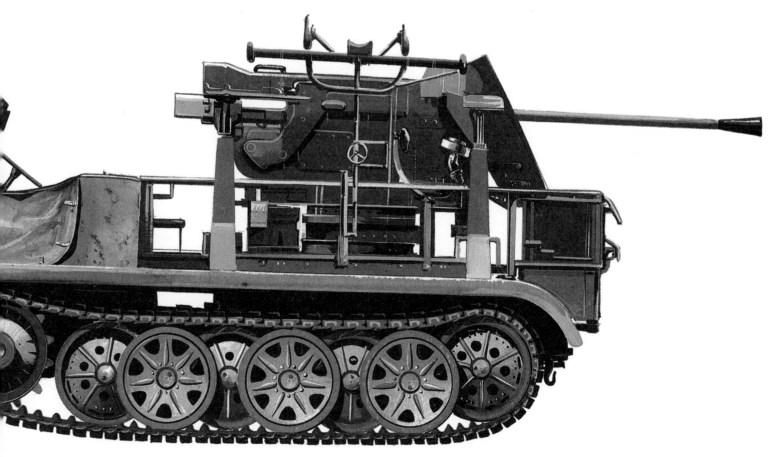

One of the most powerful tracked vehicles to see service in World War II, the SU-122 assault gun was the combination of the 121.92mm (4.8in) Field Gun Model 1931/37 (otherwise A-19) on a chassis and lower hull based on those of the KV heavy tank.

three legs and a shield. The complete equipment weighed 1,848lb (838kg), and the on-mounting elevation and traverse angles were –13 to +15 degrees and 360 degrees total respectively. The L/50 barrel had a calibre of 40mm, with no muzzle brake, and fired the 2,375lb (1,077kg) standard shot with a muzzle velocity of 2,615ft (797m) per second to penetrate 53mm (2.09in) of armour at a range of 500yds (457m) at an impact angle of 30 degrees. The weapon was very well made, but more than twice the weight of its German equivalent, which reflected a difference of tactical role envisaged by the British: the Germans planned to use their weapons offensively, in support of their own armour-led aggressive tactics, while the British planned to use their guns defensively in the prepared positions in which they would await the German attack. This was also the reason for the gun's installation on a carriage from which the two wheels could be removed, allowing the gun to settle on the ground with its tripod legs spread to provide a steady platform for fire through a traverse angle of 360 degrees. The weapon could be used in mobile warfare, either towed to a new site behind a truck or operated in the portée mode from the flatbed of a truck, but was soon rendered obsolete by the introduction of German tanks with improved armour. In the North African campaign (1940-43), the 2pdr was difficult to conceal and was soon outranged by the 50mm guns of German tanks, and it was for this reason that the 25pdr gun/howitzer was provided with anti-tank ammunition as an interim weapon pending the introduction of a more powerful specialised anti-tank gun.

The more powerful weapon was the Ordnance, QF, 6pdr that was delivered from September 1941 after a design and development process that had started in 1938. The 6pdr Mk I was essentially a development model produced only in small numbers and used mainly for training, so the first genuine production models were the 6pdr Mks II and IV that differed from each other in barrel length: the Mk II had an L/42.8 barrel while the Mk IV had an L/45 barrel, in each case without a muzzle brake. The equipment was based on a two-wheel carriage of the split-trail type with a shield, weighed 2,471lb (1,121kg), and the on-mounting elevation and traverse angles were –5 to +15 degrees and 90 degrees total respectively. The L/45 barrel had a calibre of 57mm and fired the 6.28lb (2.85kg) standard shot with a muzzle velocity of 2,700ft (823m) per second to penetrate 69mm (2.7in) of armour at a range of 1,000yds (914m) at an impact angle of 20 degrees. The anti-tank capability of the 6pdr gun was therefore considerably better than that of the 2pdr, both in terms of range and penetrable armour thickness, but the length of the equipment's development process meant that the 6pdr was obsolete within a year of its introduction. The type was also made in the USA as the 57mm Anti-Tank Gun M1.

Whereas the 2pdr and 6pdr guns were typical of British practice in being very well made weapons that were adequate for their immediate purposes, they had been designed with no real concept of the need to tackle tanks carrying considerably heavier armour than those of the current generation. The following Ordnance, QF, 17pdr was a superb weapon that was as well made as its predecessors, and was optimised for total superiority over both the current generation of tanks and those of the following generations. The weapon resulted from a March 1941 requirement for a 3in (76.2mm) anti-tank weapon, and the design and development processes of the new weapon were achieved with commendable speed so that the 17pdr entered service in August 1942 as a highly effective weapon whose capabilities were only slightly marred by the weight of its carriage, which dictated that a comparatively large crew was required for effective tactical use. The carriage was also difficult to make, and as a result the first 100 ordnances were completed before any carriages were ready for them. These ordnances were delivered to North Africa, where the obsolescence of the 6pdr was presenting major problems, and were installed on a modified version of the 25pdr gun/howitzer carriage to create an interim weapon known as the 17/25pdr. This was a moderately clumsy weapon, for the 25pdr gun/howitzer carriage could only just sustain the recoil forces generated by the 17pdr gun.

The 17pdr gun was based on a two-wheel carriage of the split-trail type with a shield, the complete equipment weighed 6,445lb (2,923kg), and the on-mounting elevation and traverse angles were –6 to +16.5 degrees and 60 degrees total respectively. The L/55.1 barrel was fitted with a double-baffle muzzle brake and fired the 17lb (7.71kg) standard shot with a muzzle velocity of 2,900ft (884m) per second to penetrate 130mm (5.12in) of armour at a range of 1,000yds at an impact angle of 30 degrees. The weapon could

Early SP Guns

THE first generations of self-propelled guns were created as expedients in the middle part of World War II, and the most important aspect of their creation was the combination of a standard piece of field artillery with a well-established medium tank chassis/hull to provide mobility for the field gun as part of the support element for armoured formations. In these circumstances a 'lash-up' design was acceptable, and this resulted in vehicles such as the American M7 and British Sexton with a simple fighting compartment able to accept the standard cradle of the selected field gun, even though this limited the on-vehicle traverse capability of the weapon and demanded a slewing of the whole vehicle to effect gross changes in bearing. This fighting compartment had to be large enough to accommodate the gun's detachment and a modest number of ready-use rounds of ammunition, and was generally designed as vertical or nearly vertical extensions of the baseline tank's upper-hull armour but without any overhead protection. Experience soon showed that the crew was inevitably vulnerable to the fragmentation effects of overhead shell bursts, and later self-propelled guns were designed with a taller fighting compartment with some measure of overhead protection.

The Sexton was a British self-propelled gun analogous to the American Howitzer Motor Carriage M7 (Priest) in that it added the 25pdr gun/howitzer to an open compartment erected on the hull and lower chassis of the Grizzly I medium tank, which was the Canadian-built version of the US M4 Sherman medium tank.

also fire a useful HE shell and was therefore effective as a dual-role anti-tank gun and field gun that remained in British service until well after the end of World War II.

The smallest of the American anti-tank guns was the 37mm Anti-Tank Gun M3, which was based on the German 37mm PaK 35/36 but with a number of important changes (including the introduction of a five-baffle muzzle brake that was later found to be unnecessary), and was mounted on the M4 series of lightweight carriage developed wholly by the Americans. The M3A1 variant that was the main production model was based on a two-wheel carriage of the split-trail type with a shield, the complete equipment weighed 912lb (414kg), and the on-mounting elevation and traverse angles were –10 to +15 degrees and 60 degrees total respectively. The L/53.5 barrel fired the 1.92lb (0.87kg) standard shot with a muzzle velocity of 2,900ft per second to penetrate 25mm (1in) of armour at a range of 1,000yds at an impact angle of 20 degrees, and could also fire an improved APC projectile to penetrate 53mm of armour at a range of 1,000yds at an impact angle of 20 degrees. Production of the M3 anti-tank gun totalled some 18,700 weapons, and although these were obsolete for use against the Germans from 1942 onwards, they were nevertheless very useful in the Pacific campaign against the Japanese until the end of World War II: the shot was capable of penetrating the armour of virtually any Japanese tank, and the weapon was also widely and successfully employed for the vital task of destroying Japanese bunkers with solid shot and repulsing Japanese massed infantry attacks with HE and canister projectiles.

Next up in size, the 57mm Anti-Tank Gun M1 was an American version of the British 6pdr. The equipment was based on a two-wheel carriage of the split-trail type with a shield and weighed 2,700lb (1,225kg), and the on-mounting elevation and traverse angles were –5 to +15 degrees and 90 degrees total respectively. The L/50 barrel had no muzzle brake and fired the 6.28lb standard shot with a muzzle velocity of 2,700ft (823m) per second to penetrate 69mm of armour at a range of 1,000yds at an impact angle of 20 degrees.

Now an obsolete type, the Creusot-Loire Mk 61 is a 105mm (4.13in) self-propelled howitzer that was designed in France during the late 1940s on the basis of the AMX-13 light tank, with its oscillating turret removed and hull rear modified into a large fixed barbette carrying the Modèle 50 howitzer in a manually operated mounting that permitted elevation in the arc between –4.5 and +66 degrees and traverse 20 degrees left and right of the centreline. The vehicle carried 56 rounds of main gun ammunition, and a local-defence capability was provided by one or two 0.3 or 0.295in (7.62 or 7.5mm) machine guns with 2,000 rounds of ammunition.

From the beginning of the 57mm Anti-Tank Gun M1 programme the Americans had realised that this could be an interim weapon at best, and by 1942 had started work on an improved weapon of indigenous design. This was the 3in (7.62mm) Anti-Tank Gun M5 that was really a judicious blend of existing components such as the barrel of the 3in Anti-Aircraft Gun M3 together with the breech mechanism, recoil system and carriage of the 105mm Howitzer M2A1. The result was a somewhat cumbersome but workable and effective weapon of which 2,500 were manufactured. The weapon was based on a two-wheel carriage of the split-trail type with a shield, the complete equipment weighed 5,850lb (2,654kg), and the on-mounting elevation and traverse angles were –5 to +30 degrees and 46 degrees total respectively. The L/50 barrel had no muzzle brake and fired the 15.43lb (7kg) standard shot with a muzzle velocity of 2,600ft (792m) per second to penetrate 98mm (3.86in) of armour at a range of 1,000yds at an impact angle of 20 degrees.

The USA made no real attempt to create and place in service any modern anti-tank guns of larger calibre, for by 1943 the US Army had decided that the anti-tank role was best fulfilled by field artillery firing heavy projectiles, and by specialised self-propelled weapons.

The smallest Soviet anti-tank gun was another copy of the German 37mm PaK 35/36, of which the Soviets bought a pilot batch before deciding on licensed manufacture for substantial numbers of a weapon known as the 37mm Anti-Tank Gun Model 1930 that differed from the German originals only in having wire-spoked wheels. Based on a two-wheel carriage of the split-trail type with a shield, the complete equipment weighed 723lb (328kg), and the on-mounting elevation and traverse angles were –8 to +25 degrees and 60 degrees total respectively. The L/45 barrel was not fitted with a muzzle brake and fired the 1.5lb standard shot with a muzzle velocity of 3,379ft (1,030m) per second to penetrate 38mm of armour at a range of 440yds at an impact angle of 30 degrees.

Like all other countries involved in the development of advanced tanks and the methods of tackling them, the USSR appreciated that the successful destruction of tanks with thicker and better disposed armour called for a

Older in concept than the Mk 61, the Creusot-Loire Mk F3 has a completely exposed mounting for its armament, which is a 155mm (6.1in) ATS gun/howitzer. This can be elevated in the arc between 0 and +67 degrees and traversed 25 degrees left and right of the centreline at lower angles of elevation, declining to 23 degrees left and right of the centreline at higher angles. The vehicle carries no ready-use ammunition; 25 rounds and the eight-man gun detachment are carried in an accompanying tracked vehicle.

The American M44 self-propelled equipment was of the fixed-barbette type, and its main armament was a 155mm (6.1in) M45 howitzer with 24 rounds of ready-use ammunition.

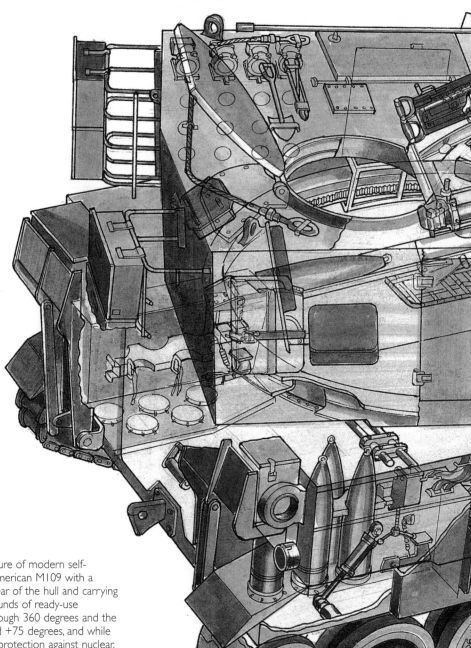

This cutaway reveals the most advanced nature of modern self-propelled equipments, in this instance the American M109 with a power operated turret mounted over the rear of the hull and carrying a 155mm (6.1in) M126 howitzer with 28 rounds of ready-use ammunition. The turret can be traversed through 360 degrees and the ordnance elevated in an arc between –3 and +75 degrees, and while earlier vehicles were not provided with any protection against nuclear, biological and chemical (NBC) warfare weapons, later variants of this still-important weapon have such protection.

two-handed approach involving the creation of anti-tank guns firing a heavier projectile at a high velocity. The first practical result of this approach was the 45mm Anti-Tank Gun Model 1932, which was in essence a scaled-up version of the ordnance of the 37mm Anti-Tank Gun Model 1930 on either of two carriage types optimised for horse and truck traction. The 45mm Anti-Tank Gun Model 1932 was based on a two-wheel carriage of the split-trail type with a shield, the complete equipment weighed 992lb (450kg) for the horse-drawn version and 1,124lb (510kg) for the truck-towed version, and the on-mounting elevation and traverse angles were –8 to +25 degrees and 60 degrees total respectively. The L/46 barrel was not fitted with a muzzle brake and fired the 3.15lb (1.43kg) standard shot with a muzzle velocity of 2,493ft (760m) per second to penetrate 38mm of armour at a range of 1,000yds at an impact angle of 30 degrees. The Model 1932 was followed by the basically similar Model 1937 that differed only in minor details and was copied by the Japanese as the 45mm Anti-Tank Gun Type 1,

This is an M109 105mm (4.13in) self-propelled howitzer of the British army. The M109A2 variant that entered service in 1979 has a turret bustle to increase the quantity of ready-use ammunition that can be carried, and other salient details of this vital Western weapon include a crew of six, weight of 55,000lb (24,948kg), length of 29ft 11in (9.12m) with the gun forward, welded aluminium armour, a powerplant of one 405hp (302kW) Detroit Diesel 8V-71T diesel engine for a maximum road speed of 35mph (56km/h) and maximum road range of 215 miles (346km), and armament of one 155mm (6.1in) M126 howitzer with 36 rounds of ammunition and one 0.5in (12.7mm) Browning machine gun with 500 rounds of ammunition.

and then by the Model 1938 with the on-mounting elevation and traverse angle altered to –10 to +10 degrees and 15 degrees total respectively, and the weight to 1,433lb (650kg). Further development of the same basic concept resulted in the 45mm Anti-Tank Gun Model 1942, which was basically the model 1937 with disc rather than spoked wheels, a lengthened barrel and a strengthened breech block. The Model 1942 was based on a two-wheel carriage of the split-trail type with a shield, the complete equipment weighed 1,257lb (570kg), and the on-mounting elevation and traverse angles were –8 to +25 degrees and 60 degrees total respectively. The L/66 barrel had no muzzle brake and fired the 3.15lb standard shot with a muzzle velocity of 2,690ft (820m) per second to penetrate 95mm (3.74in) of armour at a range of 330yds (302m).

In 1941, and just before the German invasion of their country, the Soviets introduced the 57mm Anti-Tank Gun Model 1941. This was a purpose-designed ordnance on the 76.2mm (3in) Field Gun Model 1941's two-wheel carriage of the split-trail type with a shield, the complete equipment weighed 2,480lb (1,125kg), and the on-mounting elevation and traverse angles were –10 to +18 degrees and 56 degrees total respectively. The L/73 barrel had no muzzle brake and fired the 6.94lb (3.148kg) standard shot with a muzzle velocity of 3,346ft (1,020m) per second to penetrate 140mm (5.51in) of armour at a range of 545yds. Further development resulted in the 57mm Anti-Tank Gun Model 1943, which was the same ordnance on the Model 1942's two-wheel carriage of the split-tubular trail type with a shield, the complete equipment weighed 2,535lb (1,150kg), and the on-mounting elevation and traverse angles were –5 to +25 degrees and 56 degrees total respectively.

The final Soviet anti-tank gun of World War II was the 100mm (3.94in) Anti-Tank Gun Model 1944, which was one of the most powerful weapons of its type to be developed and placed in service during the war. The ordnance was derived from that of a high-velocity naval weapon, and this was installed on a heavy carriage of the split-trail type with unusual double-tyred wheels and a shield. The complete equipment weighed 7,628lb (3,460kg), and the

The FV433 Abbot was developed by Vickers to meet a British army requirement for a light but highly mobile self-propelled howitzer. A member of the FV430 series of light armoured fighting vehicles, the FV433 uses many of the same automotive components as the FV432 armoured personnel carrier, and is armed with a 105mm (4.13in) L13A1 gun/howitzer that can be elevated in an arc between −5 and +70 degrees in a turret located over the rear of the hull and capable of traverse through 360 degrees.

on-mounting elevation and traverse angles were −5 to +45 degrees and 58 degrees total respectively. The L/59.6 barrel was fitted with a double-baffle muzzle brake and fired the 34.4lb (15.6kg) standard shot with a muzzle velocity of 2,953ft (900m) per second to penetrate 192mm (7.56in) of armour at a range of 490yds (448m).

As had been the case with field artillery weapons after World War II, the anti-tank gun entered a period of relative inactivity in terms of development and procurement, as the victorious nations were satisfied with their current equipments and saw little military advantage in adopting new equipments firing projectiles of greater weight and at higher velocity. The primary anti-tank role came to be dominated by the battle tank, in a way already foreshadowed in World War II by tanks and specialised tank destroyers, and also by the guided missile carrying a hollow-charge warhead that relies for its effect not on kinetic energy but rather on the combined chemical and physical effects of its warhead's shaping: on detonation, this vapourises a copper liner and focuses the resultant stream of violently hot gases and vaporised metal on the surface of the target armour, burning a hole through which the gas/metal stream pours to kill the crew and/or ignite the ammunition inside the tank.

This tendency toward the tank (firing a number of specialised rounds such as the HEAT type with a hollow-charge explosive filling, the HESH type with a 'pancake' of plastic explosive whose exterior detonation scales off large segments of interior armour that fly round the fighting compartment at high velocity, and the small-calibre fin-stabilised dart that penetrates the armour), the guided missile (both surface- and air-launched) and the high-velocity rocket (generally air-launched) as the primary anti-tank weapons came to assume a dominant position among the more advanced weapon-making nations in the 1950s and 1960s, although several smaller countries as well as the USSR then developed a number of large-calibre anti-tank guns that remained in service into the 1980s. Some of these weapons are detailed below by country of origin and in descending order of calibre.

The Austrian 105mm (4.13in) NORICUM ATG N 105 is a towed anti-tank

An obsolete type no longer in first-line service, the M52 was an American 105mm (4.13in) self-propelled howitzer with the M85 ordnance and 105 rounds of ammunition.

gun with an L/56.1 barrel, a split-trail carriage with two road wheels and a shield, a weight of 7,937lb (3,600kg) in travelling and firing orders, and unrevealed on-mounting elevation and traverse angles, rate of fire, range and crew. The equipment was developed initially as a mobile trials mount for NORICUM's LRN 105 long-recoil tank gun using the range of ammunition developed for the L7/M68 series of rifled tank guns, and was then evolved into a production version for countries requiring a potent anti-tank gun. Details are still sparse, but the equipment is of standard configuration with an ordnance that can be turned through 180 degrees to lie of the trail legs while being towed. The type can also fire a special NP 105 A2 armour-piercing discarding-sabot fin-stabilised (APDSFS) round whose projectile weighs 42.55lb (19.3kg) and, leaving the muzzle at a velocity of 4,872ft (1,485m) per second, can penetrate 150mm (5.91in) of armour inclined at 60 degrees at a range of 6,345yds (5,800m).

The Belgian 90mm (3.54in) MECAR KEnerga 90/46 is a towed anti-tank gun with an L/46 barrel fitted with a double-baffle muzzle brake, a split-trail carriage with two road wheels and an optional shield, a weight of 2,205lb (1,000kg), an on-mounting elevation angle of unrevealed size and an on-mounting traverse angle of 54 degrees total, a rate of fire of 10 rounds per minute (maximum) and seven rounds per minute (normal), and a crew of three or four. The equipment is a simple development of the KEnerga low recoil force rifled gun designed for use in light armoured fighting vehicles (AFVs), and its ordnance can fire nine types of fixed ammunition including APDSFS, HEAT (three varieties including one practice), HE, HESH, smoke (two varieties) and canister. The 6.02lb (2.73kg) projectile of the M603 APDSFS round leaves the muzzle at 4,692ft (1,430m) per second and can penetrate the NATO standard target armour at a range of 2,185yds (2,000m), the 9.01lb (4.085kg) projectile of the M644 HV-HEAT round leaves the muzzle at 3,346ft (1,020m) per second and can penetrate the NATO standard target armour at a range of 1,315yds (1,200m), and the

11.24lb (5.1kg) projectile of the M656 HESH round leaves the muzzle at 2,625ft (800m) per second; the M629 canister round releases 1,100 lead balls with a muzzle velocity of 2,543ft (775m) per second.

Another Belgian weapon, the 90mm Field Mount is a towed anti-tank gun with an L/32.2 barrel with no muzzle brake, has a three-leg (tripod) type of carriage with two road wheels and a shield, weighs 1,940lb (880kg), possesses on-mounting elevation and traverse angles of –10 to +12 degrees and 360 degrees total respectively, has a rate of fire of 18 rounds per minute (maximum) and 10 rounds per minute (normal), and is operated by a crew of three or four. The equipment is based on the 90mm MECAR anti-tank gun that was designed for installation in light armoured vehicles but, in this application, is fitted on a towed carriage with twin road wheels that lift to allow the folding tripod legs to be opened out for 360-degree traverse. The fixed ammunition options are HEAT-CAN-90 anti-tank with a 5.4lb (2.45kg) projectile fired at a muzzle velocity of 2,077ft (633m) per second to penetrate 375mm (14.76in) of armour at a range of 1,095yds (1,000m), HE-CAN-90 anti-personnel with an 8.8lb (4kg) projectile fired at a muzzle velocity of 1,109ft (338m) per second for a range of 3,280yds (3,000m), CNT-CAN-90 canister with an effective range of 275yds (250m), and smoke.

The Chinese 100mm (3.94in) NORINCO Anti-Tank Gun Type 86 is a towed anti-tank gun with a barrel of unrevealed length fitted with a multi-baffle muzzle brake, is carried on a split-trail carriage with two road wheels and a shield, weighs 8,069lb (3,660kg), has on-mounting elevation and traverse angles of –4 to +38 degrees and 50 degrees total respectively,

Seen here in the form of an equipment in British service, the M107 175mm (6.89in) self-propelled gun was designed for the long-range bombardment of tactically and operationally important targets deep in the enemy's rear area. The M113 gun, for which only two rounds of ready-use ammunition are carried, can deliver accurate fire to a maximum range of 35,750yds (32,690m), and the detachment and additional ammunition are carried in an accompanying tracked vehicle.

possesses a rate of fire of between eight and 10 rounds per minute, has a range of 14,930yds (13,650m), and is served by a crew of unknown number. The equipment was introduced in 1987 as a simple yet effective anti-tank gun that is apparently based on the combination of a new smooth-bore ordnance on the carriage of the Type 56 field gun. The weapon is designed primarily for the direct-fire role, but indirect-fire sights are fitted for fire to a maximum range limited by the equipment's low maximum elevation; the type can also be fitted with a night vision device. No details of the ammunition have yet been revealed, although the use of a smooth-bore barrel suggests that the primary round is an APDSFS type firing a sub-calibre dart at very high velocity.

Another Chinese equipment, the 85mm (3.35in) NORINCO Gun Type 56 is a towed field and anti-tank gun with an L/55.2 barrel fitted with a double-baffle muzzle brake, carried on a split-trail carriage with two road wheels and (on some equipments) one castor plus a shield, weighing 3,858lb (1,750kg), possessing on-mounting elevation and traverse angles of –7 to +35 degrees and 54 degrees total respectively, characterised by a rate of fire of between 15 and 20 rounds per minute, having a range of 17,115yds (15,650m), and served by a crew of between six and eight. This equipment is essentially the Soviet D-44 gun built with slight modification in China. The ordnance can fire HE, HEAT and HESH rounds, and is thus used mainly as a support and anti-tank weapon. The HEAT projectile weighs 15.43lb (7kg) and at a range of 1,060yds (970m) can penetrate 100mm (3.94in) of armour at an angle of 65 degrees.

The Czechoslovak 100mm (3.94in) M53 field and anti-tank gun is a towed equipment with an L/67.35 barrel fitted with a double-baffle muzzle brake. The gun is installed on a split-trail carriage with two road wheels and two castors plus a shield, weighs 9,436lb (4,280kg) in travelling order and 9,281lb (4,210kg) in firing position, has on-mounting elevation and traverse angles of –6 to +42 degrees and 60 degrees total respectively, possesses a

The M109G is the version of the M109 155mm (6.1in) self-propelled howitzer family for the German army, with a number of German features (including the tracks of the Leopard 1 main battle tank) and a revised breech increasing the standard range of the M126 ordnance from 16,000 to 20,230yds (14,630 to 18,500m).

rate of fire of between eight and 10 rounds per minute, has a range of 22,965yds (21,000m), and is served by a crew of six. The M53 was introduced in the early 1950s, and is a dual-purpose field and anti-tank gun firing fixed ammunition including a 35.3lb (16kg) APC-T projectile at a muzzle velocity of 3,281ft (1,000m) per second to penetrate 185mm (7.28in) of armour at a range of 1,095yds, a 27.25lb (12.36kg) HEAT-FS projectile at a muzzle velocity of 2,953ft (900m) per second to penetrate 380mm (14.96in) of armour at any range, a 12.54lb (5.69kg) HVAPDS-T projectile at a muzzle velocity of 4,642ft (1,415m) per second to penetrate 200mm (7.87in) of armour at a range of 1,095yds, and a 34.37lb (15.59kg) FRAG-HE projectile at a muzzle velocity of 2,953ft per second.

Another Czechoslovak weapon, the 85mm M52/55 85mm field and anti-tank gun is a towed equipment with an L/59.65 barrel fitted with a double-baffle muzzle brake, and its other details include a split-trail carriage with two road wheels and a shield, a weight of 4,780lb (2,168kg) in travelling order and 4,654lb (2,111kg) in firing position, on-mounting elevation and traverse angles of –6 to +38 degrees and 60 degrees total respectively, a rate of fire of 20 rounds per minute, a range of 17,675yds (16,160m), and a crew of seven. Introduced in 1952, this is a dual-purpose field and anti-tank gun, and among the fixed ammunition types available are AP-T with a 20.28lb (9.2kg) projectile fired at a muzzle velocity of 2,690ft (820m) per second to penetrate 123mm (4.84in) of armour at a range of 1,095yds, HEAT-FS, HVAP-T and HE. The M52/55 is an improved model of 1955 with the slightly greater weights.

The Swiss 90mm (3.54in) Federal Construction M57 is a towed anti-tank gun with an L/33.7 barrel fitted with a multi-baffle muzzle brake, and its other details include a split-trail carriage with two road wheels and a shield, a weight of 1,323lb (600kg) in travelling order and 1,257lb (570kg) in firing position, on-mounting elevation and traverse angles of –15 to +23 degrees and 70 degrees total up to +11 degrees elevation and 44 degrees total over 11 degrees elevation, a rate of fire of 20 rounds per minute (maximum) and six rounds per minute (normal), a range of 3,280yds overall, 985yds (900m) against a static target or 765yds (700m) against a moving target, and a crew of five. Introduced in 1958, this light anti-tank equipment fires a 5.95lb (2.7kg) HEAT projectile at a muzzle velocity of 1,969ft (600m) per second to penetrate 250mm (9.84in) of armour.

Another Swiss equipment, the 90mm Federal Construction M50 is a towed anti-tank gun with an L/32.2 barrel with no muzzle brake, and its other details include a split-trail carriage with two road wheels and a shield, a weight of 1,323lb (600kg) in travelling order and 1,226lb (556kg) in firing position, on-mounting elevation and traverse angles of –10 to +32 degrees and 66 degrees total up to +11 degrees elevation and 34 degrees total over 11 degrees elevation, a rate of fire of 20 rounds per minute (maximum) and six rounds per minute (normal), a range of 3,280yds overall, or 765yds against a static target or 545yds against a moving target, and a crew of five. Introduced in 1953, this light anti-tank equipment fires a 4.3lb (1.95kg) HEAT projectile at a muzzle velocity of 1,969ft per second to penetrate 250mm of armour.

The Soviet 100mm (3.94in) T-12 is a towed anti-tank gun with an L/84.8 barrel fitted with a 'pepperpot' muzzle brake, and its other details include a split-trail carriage with two road wheels and a shield, a weight of 6,614lb (3,000kg), on-mounting elevation and traverse angles of –10 to +20 degrees and 27 degrees total respectively, a rate of fire of 10 rounds per minute, a range of 9,295yds (8,500m), and a crew of six. Designed as successor to the 85mm D-48 anti-tank gun, the T-12 was introduced in the mid-1960s and uses fixed ammunition of two types, namely APDSFS with a 12.13lb (5.5kg)

Modern SP Guns

WHEREAS early self-propelled guns were usually based on tank chassis, modern equipments are generally based on a purpose-designed chassis carrying only comparatively light armour as the vehicle's long-range armament makes it possible to operate at a greater remove from the enemy, and the chassis generally makes extensive use of automotive components from tanks and armoured personnel carriers for improved commonality and thus a simplification of the vehicle's required logistical infrastructure. In basic design the modern SP equipment is similar to the tank with a turret capable of 360 degrees traverse, although this turret is somewhat larger and generally located farther to the rear. The additional size is required by the turret to accommodate the larger breech of the greater-calibre gun and the larger detachment needed to work the gun, although the size of the detachment can be reduced by the use of an automatic loading system that permits the equipment to maintain a higher rate of fire. Among the equipment virtually standard in modern self-propelled artillery are an NBC warfare protection package based on sealed driving and fighting compartments provided with filtered air, a land navigation system for a high degree of accuracy in spotting the equipment's position relative to its target, passive night driving gear, and an advanced fire-control system based on a digital computer to work out the solution to any fire-control problem on the basis of the vehicle's position and two-dimensional tilt, ambient air temperature, direction and speed, projectile type and ammunition charge used, and con-tinuously updated muzzle velocity.

projectile fired at a muzzle velocity of 4,921ft (1,500m) per second to penetrate 406mm (16in) of armour at a range of 545yds, and HEAT with a 20.94lb (9.5kg) projectile fired at a muzzle velocity of 3,248ft (990m) per second to penetrate 400mm (15.75in) of armour at any range up to 1,310yds (1,200m). The T-12A is a modified version with larger wheels and a weight of 6,834lb (3,100kg).

The Soviet 100mm BS-3 is a towed field and anti-tank gun with an L/60.7 barrel fitted with a double-baffle muzzle brake, and its other details include a split-trail carriage with two twin road wheels and a shield, a weight of 8,047lb (3,650kg), on-mounting elevation and traverse angles of –5 to +45 degrees and 58 degrees total respectively, a rate of fire of between eight and 10 rounds per minute, a range of 22,965yds, and a crew of six. Introduced in 1944 as the Model 1944 (see above), this powerful weapon was later upgraded to fire more modern fixed ammunition types including a 34.4lb (15.6kg) HE-FRAG type fired at a muzzle velocity of 2,953ft (900m) per second, a 35.3lb (16kg) APC-T type fired at a muzzle velocity of 3,281ft per second to penetrate 185mm (7.28in) of armour at a range of 1,095yds, a 12.54lb (5.69kg) HVAPDS-T type fired at a muzzle velocity 4,642ft (1,415m) per second to penetrate more than 200mm (7.87in) of armour at a range of 1,095yds, and a 27.25lb (12.36kg) HEAT-FS type fired at a muzzle velocity of 2,953ft per second to penetrate 380mm (14.96in) of armour at any range up to 1,095yds. Type 59 Anti-Tank Gun is the provisional designation of the Chinese copy of the BS-3, adopted as successor to the 85mm Type 56 as an anti-tank and counter-battery weapon: the equipment's weight is estimated at 7,606lb (3,450kg), and the AP-T projectile's penetration is thought to be 157mm (6.18in) of armour at a range of 1,095yds.

The American M110 8in (203mm) self-propelled howitzer is based on the same chassis as the M107 175mm (6.89in) self-propelled gun, and can fire a 204lb (92.53kg) HE projectile with a muzzle velocity of 1,925ft (587m) per second to a maximum range of 18,400yds (16,825m). The long range of the ordnances carried by the M110 and M107 was the reason that the Americans decided that enclosed accommodation was unnecessary on the grounds that the crews would never come under fire from the enemy.

The Soviet 85mm SD-44 is a towed field and anti-tank gun with an L/53 barrel fitted with a double-baffle muzzle brake, and among its other details are a split-trail carriage with an auxiliary power unit, two road wheels and one castor plus a shield, a weight of 4,960lb (2,250kg), on-mounting elevation and traverse angles of –7 to +35 degrees and 54 degrees total respectively, a rate of fire of 15 rounds per minute (bursts) and 10 rounds per minute (sustained fire), a range of 17,115yds (15,650m), and a crew of seven. The SD-44 is essentially the D-44 divisional gun fitted with a 14hp (10.4kW) M-72 petrol-engined auxiliary power unit to provide airborne formations with a relatively powerful ordnance possessing limited self-mobility at a maximum road speed of 15.5mph (25km/h). The ordnance fires fixed ammunition, and the projectiles include a 21.2lb (9.6kg) HE-FRAG type fired at a muzzle velocity of 2,598ft (792m) per second, a 20.3lb (9.2kg) AP-T type fired at the same muzzle velocity to penetrate 125mm (4.92in) of armour at a range of 1,095yds, an 11.16lb (5.06kg) HVAP-T type fired at a muzzle velocity of 3,379ft per second to penetrate 180mm (7.09in) of armour at a range of 1,095yds, and a 16.2lb (7.34kg) HEAT-FS type fired at a muzzle velocity of 2,756ft (840m) per second to penetrate 300mm (11.8in) of armour at any range.

The Soviet 85mm D-48 is a towed anti-tank gun with an L/74 barrel fitted with a 'pepperpot' muzzle brake, and among its other details are a split-trail carriage with two road wheels and one castor plus a shield, a weight of 5,181lb (2,350kg), on-mounting elevation and traverse angles of –6 to +35 degrees and 54 degrees total respectively, a rate of fire of 15 rounds per minute (bursts) and eight rounds per minute (sustained fire), a range of 20,745yds (18,970m), and a crew of six. The D-48 was originally thought by

The FV433 is now out of first-line service, but in its time was an effective self-propelled system in which the small calibre of the ordnance was offset by its very considerable accuracy, resulting largely from Vickers' long experience with naval guns including the current 4.5in (114.3mm) weapon from which the Abbot's gun was derived.

Based on the well-proved chassis of the ZRK Krug self-propelled surface-to-air missile system with its SA-4 'Ganef' missile, the 2S3 Akatsiya is a 152mm (6in) self-propelled gun/howitzer now in Russian service. The whole equipment is very neat and possesses both an NBC protection system and passive night driving gear, but is not amphibious.

the West to be a 100mm (3.94in) weapon when introduced in the mid-1950s, and it does indeed use a 100mm type of fixed round, although necked down in this application for an 85mm (3.35in) projectile, in the form of either a 21.4lb (9.7kg) APHE type fired at a muzzle velocity of 3,281ft per second to penetrate 190mm (7.48in) of armour at a range of 1,095yds or a 20.5lb (9.3kg) HVAP type fired at a muzzle velocity of some 3,937ft (1,200m) per second to penetrate 240mm (9.45in) of armour at the same range.

Yet another Soviet type, the 57mm Ch-26 is a towed anti-tank gun with an L/71.4 barrel fitted with a double-baffle muzzle brake, and among its other details are a split-trail carriage with an auxiliary power unit and three road wheels plus a shield, a weight of 2,756lb (1,250kg), on-mounting elevation and traverse angles of –4 to +15 degrees and 56 degrees total respectively, a rate of fire of 12 rounds per minute, a range of 7,325yds (6,700m), and a crew of five. Designed for use by airborne formations, the Ch-26 remains in second-line service with a few countries, and features a 14hp (10.4kW) petrol-engined auxiliary power unit to provide a maximum road speed of 25mph (40km/h). The ordnance uses fixed ammunition whose projectiles include an 8.27lb (3.75kg) HE-FRAG type fired with a muzzle velocity of 2,280ft (695m) per second, a 6.92lb (3.14kg) AP-T type fired with a muzzle velocity of 3,215ft (980m) per second to penetrate 106mm (4.17in) of armour at a range of 545yds, and a 3.88lb (1.76kg) HVAP-T type fired at a muzzle velocity of 4,117ft (1,255m) per second to penetrate 140mm (5.51in) of armour at a range of 545yds.

The growing importance of aircraft in warfare during the 1920s and 1930s, together with their steadily improving performance, paved the way during the 1930s for the development of specialised anti-aircraft guns, which were altogether more capable than the extemporised weapons of World War I. The increasing number of roles that could be undertaken by such warplanes also demanded the creation of anti-aircraft guns dedicated to specific parts of the air-defence spectrum, ranging from small-calibre weapons capable of generating an increasingly dense 'wall of fire' to defeat low-level tactical aircraft, to medium-calibre weapons designed to tackle high-flying strategic bombers with HE-FRAG shells capable of reaching an altitude of 20,000ft (6,095m) . Yet again, it was Germany, the UK, the USA and the USSR that predominated in the development and construction of such weapons, although two neutral countries – Sweden and Switzerland – had been responsible respectively for the creation of 40mm and 20mm weapons that were widely used by most of the combatants.

Germany's smallest-calibre anti-aircraft gun was a Rheinmetall design, the 20mm Fliegerabwehrkanone (FlaK) 30 that was developed from the Solothurn S5-100 (otherwise ST-5) for a service debut in 1935. The weapon was reliable, but possessed only a modest rate of fire and was prone to jamming under certain conditions, and was built in very large numbers for use by all the German armed forces. The details of this weapon included an L/115 barrel fitted with a flash suppressor to fire a 0.2625lb (0.119kg) HE projectile with a muzzle velocity of 2,953ft (900m) per second, a two-wheel carriage with a Y-type trail fitted with a stabilising leg carrying the weapon that could be dismounted to rest on a tripod platform, a weight of 1,698lb (770kg) in travelling order and 992lb (450kg) in firing position, on-mounting elevation and traverse angles of –12 to +90 degrees and 360 degrees total respectively, a rate of fire of 280 rounds per minute (cyclic) or 120 rounds per minute (practical), an effective ceiling of 6,630ft (2,020m), and a crew of five or six.

The FlaK 30's indifferent rate of fire and tendency to jam caused considerable concern in German military circles, and the task of improving the weapon was entrusted to Mauser, which completed the task in 1940 with the creation of the 20mm FlaK 38 with a revised breech mechanism that increased the cyclic rate of fire by some 70 per cent. The details of this weapon included an L/112.6 barrel fitted with a flash suppressor to fire a 0.2625lb HE projectile with a muzzle velocity of 2,953ft per second, a weight of 1,654lb (750kg) in travelling order and 926lb (420kg) in firing position, on-mounting elevation and traverse angles of –20 to +90 degrees and 360 degrees total respectively, a rate of fire of 420 to 480 rounds per minute (cyclic) or 180 to 220 rounds per minute (practical), an effective ceiling of 6,630ft, and a crew of five or six.

A massive equipment offering excellent capabilities, the French GIAT GCT is a 155mm (6.1in) self-propelled howitzer based on the chassis of the AMX-30 main battle tank, and therefore offering full tactical compatibility with the armoured formations it was designed to support.

The odd appearance of the Bofors Bandkanon 1A, a 155mm (6.1in) self-propelled howitzer of Swedish design and construction, results from the use of a chassis based on that of the Strv 103 main battle tank surmounted by a comparatively small turret but large backward-projecting automatic loading system, which allows a high rate of fire with a 14-round ammunition clip that can be replenished in a mere two minutes.

The same 20mm calibre was retained for one of Germany's most formidable light anti-aircraft equipments, the Flakvierling 38 that was designed by Mauser as a four-barrel weapon for the defence of high-value targets. The weapon was originally developed for the German navy, with which it entered service in the late 1930s, and was then adopted by the German army and air force in 1940. So successful was the type that production was steadily increased, reaching a maximum of 410 per month during 1944. The equipment was basically four FlaK 38 barrels on a revised version of the FlaK 38's carriage, and its details included four L/112.6 barrels each fitted with a flash suppressor to fire a 0.2625lb HE projectile with a muzzle velocity of 2,953ft per second, a weight of 4,878lb (2,212kg) in travelling order and 3,338lb (1,514kg) in firing position, on-mounting elevation and traverse angles of –10 to +100 degrees and 360 degrees total respectively, a rate of fire of 1,800 rounds per minute (cyclic) or 880 rounds per minute (practical), an effective ceiling of 6,630ft, and a crew of seven.

These 20mm weapons were necessarily limited in effective ceiling and shell destructiveness, so the equipments of this calibre were complemented by 37mm weapons firing a larger and more potent shell to a greater effective ceiling. The first of these weapons was the 37mm FlaK 18 developed by Rheinmetall on the basis of the Solothurn S10-100 (otherwise ST-10). The equipment entered service in 1935 basically for ground use, with the weapon carried above a cruciform firing platform that was lowered to the ground once the four wheels had been removed, but there were a number of problems with the gun and its carriage and production was therefore ended after the delivery of only a few weapons, whose details included an L/98 barrel fitted with a flash suppressor to fire a 1.4lb (0.64kg) HE projectile with a muzzle velocity of 2,689ft (820m) per second, a weight of 8,013lb (3,634kg) in travelling order and 3,859lb (1,750kg) in firing position, on-mounting elevation and traverse angles of –8 to +85 degrees and 360 degrees total respectively, a rate of fire of 160 rounds per minute (cyclic) or 80 rounds per minute (practical), a maximum ceiling of 11,565ft (3,525m), and a crew of seven.

Early anti-aircraft guns of the mobile type, designed principally to provide a capability against airships and slow-flying bombers rather than tactical aircraft, were basically light field guns installed on the flatbeds of conventional trucks. A good example is that illustrated here, which was a British equipment using a Peerless truck carrying an 18pdr field gun with a barrel liner reducing the calibre to 3in (76.2mm) to permit the high-velocity firing of a 13pdr shell by an 18pdr cartridge.

The FlaK 18's successors were the closely related FlaK 36 and 37 equipments, which entered production in 1936 with the same ordnance as the FlaK 18, with the exception of a shortened chamber firing a projectile with one rather than two driving bands, but carried on an improved two-wheel carriage. The FlaK 37 was basically identical to the FlaK 36 except for its sight, which was a clockwork-powered Zeiss unit. The details of this weapon included an L/98 barrel fitted with a flash suppressor to fire a 1.4lb HE projectile with a muzzle velocity of 2,689ft per second, a weight of 5,292lb (2,400kg) in travelling order and 3,418lb (1,550kg) in firing position, on-mounting elevation and traverse angles of –8 to +85 degrees and 360 degrees total respectively, a rate of fire of 160 rounds per minute (cyclic) or 80 rounds per minute (practical), a maximum ceiling of 15,750ft (4,800m), and a crew of seven.

Introduced in the mid-war years as another Rheinmetall design, the 37mm FlaK 43 used basically the same barrel and exactly the same ammunition as the FlaK 36 and 37 weapons, in combination with a new gas-operated breech mechanism. The type was carried on a two-wheel carriage which was removed to allow the equipment to rest on the ground on its tripod firing platform, and the introduction of a number of manufacturing changes reduced the manhours required for the construction of each equipment from 4,320 to 1,000. The details of this weapon included an L/89.2 barrel fitted with a flash suppressor to fire a 1.4lb HE projectile with a muzzle velocity of 2,757ft (840m) per second, a weight of 2,690lb (1,220kg), on-mounting elevation and traverse angles of –7 to +90 degrees and 360 degrees total respectively, a rate of fire of 250 rounds per minute (cyclic) or 150 to 180 rounds per minute (practical), a maximum ceiling of 15,750ft, and a crew of six or seven.

The 37mm Flakzwilling 43 was a development of the FlaK 43 with two superimposed barrels for a doubling of the rate of fire. The details of this weapon included an L/89.2 barrel fitted with a flash suppressor to fire a 1.4lb HE projectile with a muzzle velocity of 2,757ft per second, a weight of 10,694lb (4,850kg) in travelling order and 5,511lb (2,500kg) in firing position, on-mounting elevation and traverse angles of –7 to +90 degrees and 360 degrees total respectively, a rate of fire of 500 rounds per minute (cyclic) or 300 to 350 rounds per minute (practical), and a maximum ceiling of 15,750ft.

The Germans also tried to develop anti-aircraft guns in 50mm calibre to fulfil the medium-altitude role, but the 50mm FlaK 41 was unsuccessful, and the 50mm FlaK 214 was about to enter service as World War II ended. The 75mm (2.95in) FlaK L/60 was a Krupp design manufactured in small quantities by Bofors in Sweden and mostly for the export market after Germany had rejected the weapon, but a few such equipments were used by the German navy for the protection of its bases in World War II.

After the initial rejection of its 75mm weapon, the Krupp design team turned its attention to an 88mm (3.465in) weapon at the beginning of a process that resulted in one of Germany's most celebrated weapons of World War II. This was the 88mm FlaK 18 that was designed for road movement on a four-wheel carriage whose axles were removed once the firing position had been reached, to permit the weapon to be emplaced on a cruciform firing platform carrying a central pedestal supporting the ordnance proper. This was an exceptional piece of work designed for decisive effect against current and all foreseeable targets. The design team decided that despite the size of the weapon and the potent shell it fired, as high a rate of fire as possible was still desirable, and for this reason the FlaK 18 was completed with a semi-automatic breech mechanism. The FlaK 18 was blooded in the Spanish Civil War, where its utility as a dual-role anti-tank and anti-aircraft weapon was realised as a result of emergency use in the anti-tank role, and the main run of these important weapons was therefore completed with a shield, a surface-to-surface sight and AP40 type anti-tank projectiles. The details of this weapon included an L/56 barrel firing a 20.34lb (9.23kg) HE projectile with a muzzle velocity of 2,689ft (820m) per second, a weight of 15,129lb (6,861kg) in travelling order, on-mounting elevation and traverse angles of –3 to +85 degrees and 360 degrees total respectively, a maximum ceiling of 26,245ft (8,000m), and a crew of 10.

The FlaK 18 was followed into production by the 88mm FlaK 36 and 37 weapons. The FlaK 36 was a development of the FlaK 18 with an improved carriage supported by double- rather than single-tyred wheels, and with a Rheinmetall-designed system of three removable barrel liners that could be changed in the field, to avoid changing the whole barrel when this became worn. The FlaK 37 was a development of the FlaK 36 with a revised data-transmission system that effectively precluded the weapon from use in the anti-tank role. In all other essential respects, the FlaK 36 and 37 were identical to the FlaK 18.

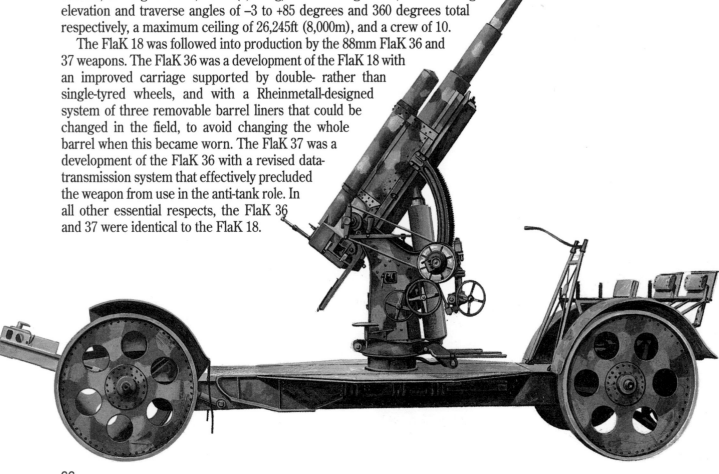

The Germans' last anti-aircraft gun of World War I was this Krupp 80mm (3.15in) weapon pedestal mounted on a four-wheel trailer for a high angle of elevation and 360 degrees traverse.

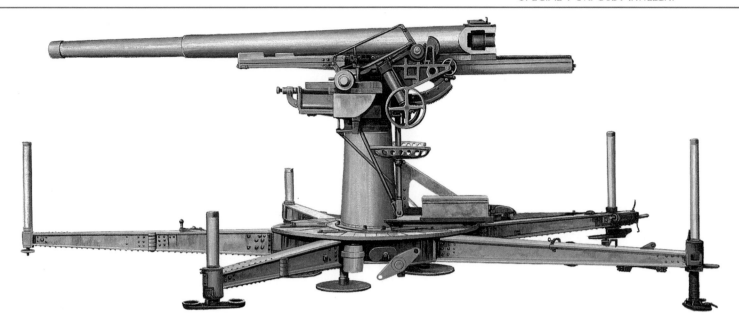

One of the most widely used of all Japanese anti-aircraft guns of World War II was the Army 75mm Mobile Field Anti-Aircraft Gun Type 88 that was introduced in 1928 and proved capable of delivering its 14.5lb (6.58kg) projectile to a maximum effective ceiling of 23,700ft (7,230m) after it had left the muzzle at a velocity of 2,360ft (720m) per second.

By the time of the outbreak of World War II, it was clear that while the first three generations of 88mm guns offered exceptional capabilities, their superiority would inevitably be eroded by the development of aircraft flying at greater speeds and higher altitudes, and in 1939 Rheinmetall was therefore instructed to start on the design and development of an improved anti-aircraft gun that retained the 88mm calibre. The first prototype weapons were completed in 1941, resulting in the designation FlaK 41, but it was 1943 before the first equipments entered full service as there were considerable problems to be overcome in the equipment's systems and its several untried features. Two of these features, incorporated specifically to provide the FlaK 41 with an anti-tank capability, were a turntable rather than pedestal carriage and a separate firing circuit for the anti-tank role. Once the teething problems had been eliminated, the FlaK 41 matured rapidly as so exceptional an anti-aircraft weapon that the type was seldom used in anything but this role. The details of this weapon included an L/74 barrel fitted to fire a 20.69lb (9.4kg) HE projectile with a muzzle velocity of 3,281ft per second, a weight of 24,784lb (11,240kg) in travelling order and 17,287lb (7,840kg) in firing position, on-mounting elevation and traverse angles of –3 to +90 degrees and 360 degrees total respectively, and a maximum ceiling of 49,215ft (15,000m).

The excellent 88mm weapons were not the last word in German anti-aircraft thinking, however, for as early as 1933 the Germans had foreseen the development of bombers and strategic reconnaissance aircraft able to fly too fast and too high for successful engagement with the 88mm weapon, and therefore ordered the start of work on a 105mm weapon. This task was entrusted to Krupp and Rheinmetall, which were each instructed to complete prototype weapons for comparative evaluation in 1935. The Rheinmetall type was deemed superior and ordered into production during 1936 as the 105mm FlaK 38. This looked as though it was merely a scaled-up 88mm weapon, but in fact there were many important changes in details such as the electrical control system, and the loading mechanism that was so effective that it was later adapted for the FlaK 41. Development changes included a major modification of the electrical control system and the introduction of a two-section barrel, and the change of the data-transmission system from that used in the 88mm FlaK 18 and 36 to that employed in the FlaK 37, and with these changes the FlaK 38 became the FlaK 39. The performance of these 105mm weapons was later overtaken by that of the

88mm FlaK 41, but production of the larger-calibre weapon was continued as production of the smaller-calibre weapon was never enough to satisfy demand. The details of this weapon included an L/63 barrel firing a 33.3lb (15.1kg) HE projectile with a muzzle velocity of 2,886ft (880m) per second, a weight of 32,193lb (14,600kg) in travelling order and 22,579lb (10,240kg) in firing position, on-mounting elevation and traverse angles of –3 to +85 degrees and 360 degrees total respectively, a maximum ceiling of 42,000ft (12,800m), and a crew of 12.

The largest calibre used by the Germans for an anti-aircraft weapon was 128mm (5.04in), and in this calibre there were two exceptional weapons, namely the FlaK 40 and the Flakzwilling 40. The FlaK 40 was ordered from Rheinmetall in 1936, and first appeared in prototype form during 1937. Only six of the type were initially produced, and in a mobile form (first in two loads and then as a single load), but from 1942 the type was built exclusively for fixed use, as the smaller and lighter 88mm FlaK 41 was generally better for the mobile role. The 128mm (5.04in) FlaK 40 was used mainly for the protection of high-value sites in Germany, and used a combination of electrical controls and electrical ramming. The details of this weapon included an L/61 barrel firing a 57.3lb (26kg) HE projectile with a muzzle velocity of 2,886ft (880m) per second, a weight of 28,660lb (13,000kg) in fixed form, on-mounting elevation and traverse angles of –3 to +88 degrees and 360 degrees total respectively, a maximum ceiling of 48,555ft (14,800m), and a crew of 10in 1936 a 150mm (5.91in) anti-aircraft gun was ordered from Krupp for installation on FlaK towers especially built around Berlin and other major German cities. The design and development of this gun was so slow that the type was cancelled, however, in favour of a twin version of the FlaK 40 with two guns side-by-side on an enlarged cradle. Comparatively few of these exceptionally powerful equipments were produced, with details that included an L/61 barrel firing a 57.3lb HE projectile with a muzzle velocity of 2,886ft per second, a weight of 59,524lb (27,000kg), on-mounting elevation and traverse angles of 0 to +88 degrees and 360 degrees total respectively, and a maximum ceiling of 48,555ft.

As with the Germans, the smallest calibre used by the British for a dedicated anti-aircraft gun was 20mm. The most common weapon in this calibre was the Polsten, whose unusual name stems from the fact that the design of the cannon originated in Poland (as a simplified version of the Swiss Oerlikon that would therefore be easier and cheaper to make) but was completed in the UK by Czechoslovak and British designers for manufacture by the Sten organisation. The result was a weapon offering

The single most important tactical anti-aircraft gun used by the Allies in World War II was the 40mm Bofors gun designed in Sweden but built under licence in the UK, the USA and in other countries. The details of this vital weapon, in its British-built Ordnance, QF, Bofors Anti-Aircraft Gun Mk I form on a four-wheel towed carriage, included an L/56 barrel, weight of 5,418lb (2,457kg), elevation in an arc between –5 and +90 degrees, traverse through 360 degrees, rate of fire of 120 rounds per minute (cyclic) or 60-90 rounds per minute (practical), and muzzle velocity of 2,800ft (854m) per second to deliver its 1.96lb (0.89kg) projectile to a maximum ceiling of 23,600ft (7,200m). The detachment numbered some five or six men including two who loaded the four-round ammunition clips into the overhead feed stay.

basically the same capabilities as the Oerlikon for a manufacturing cost of a mere £70 rather than the Swiss weapon's £320, due to the fact that the number of components had been reduced from 250 to 119 and that many of these components required considerably less or even no machining. The first such weapons were delivered in March 1944, and from that time the Polsten generally replaced the Oerlikon for land use. The type was supplied with ammunition from a 30-round box magazine inserted over the weapon, and its other details included an L/72.4 barrel firing a 0.2625lb HE projectile with a muzzle velocity of 2,725ft per second, an on-mounting traverse angle of 360 degrees total, a rate of fire of 450 rounds per minute (cyclic), a maximum ceiling of 6,630ft (2,020m), and a crew of two.

There was then a considerable gap in calibre (with the exception of a few Vickers 40mm weapons) up to the size of the 3in (76.2mm) Ordnance, QF, 3in, 20cwt, that was introduced in World War I but was built in a number of steadily improved marks for service through World War II until its retirement in 1946. This was an unexceptional weapon, and the details for the 3in Gun Mk IIIA on the Mk 1 four-wheeled carriage included an L/46.6 barrel firing a 16lb HE projectile with a muzzle velocity of 2,000ft (610m) per second, a weight of 17,584lb (7,976kg), on-mounting elevation and traverse angles of –10 to +90 degrees and 360 degrees total respectively, and a maximum ceiling of 23,500ft (7,165m).

The weapon designed to supersede the 3in weapon, although it did not achieve this objective until after World War II and was generally disliked for the fact that it was heavier and more difficult to handle than its predecessor, was the 3.7in (94mm) Ordnance, QF, 3.7in. The need for an anti-aircraft gun in this calibre had been suggested as early as 1920, but it was not until 1937 that the War Office issued the requirement for this specific weapon. A design by Vickers was approved in 1934, and the first prototype weapon was completed in April 1936. Trials revealed the satisfactory nature of the weapon, and the first production weapons were delivered in January 1938. The ordnance was a maximum yet basically straightforward unit, but the carriage was highly complex and the delivery of completed equipments was delayed by the fact that the carriages were being completed at a slower rate than the ordnances. The ordnance was eventually evolved through three marks and was of modern design with a liner that could be changed whenever it became worn, and was planned for movement on a four-wheeled carriage that was so heavy that the complete equipment was little more than semi-mobile. Other companies were brought into the programme to produce fixed mountings for the ordnance, and as a result there were the Mks I, IA, III and IIIA mobile mountings with four-wheeled carriages as well as the Mks II, IIA, IIB and IIC fixed mountings. The later ordnances were characterised by the incorporation of a power rammer and an automatic fuse setter, and other features included a data-transmission system and a predictor. The details of the Ordnance, QF, 3.7in, Mk III on Mounting Mk III included an L/50 barrel firing a 28.56lb (12.95kg) HE projectile with a muzzle velocity of 2,600ft (793m) per second, a weight of 20,541lb (9,317kg) in travelling order, on-mounting elevation and traverse angles of –5 to +80 degrees and 360 degrees total respectively, and a maximum ceiling of 32,000ft (9,755m).

The only other British anti-aircraft gun designed for land use was the 3.7in Ordnance, QF, 3.7in Mk 6, although it should be noted that two naval equipments were also adapted for land use as the 4.5in (114.3mm) Ordnance, QF, 4.5in, ANTI-AIRCRAFT, Mk II and the 5.25in (133.35mm) Ordnance, QF, 5.25in, ANTI-AIRCRAFT, Mk II. The 3.7in Mk 6 equipment resulted from an official requirement of 1940 for a gun providing a capability against bombers flying as high as 50,000ft (15,240m), and the requirement demanded that the shell reach this altitude in a time of 45 seconds (later reduced to 30 seconds as a means of simplifying the solution of the already complex fire-control problem), and that the guns be capable of firing three rounds every 20 seconds. One of the two equipments adopted to meet this requirement was the 5.25in weapon named above, and the other was a 4.5in weapon lined down to a calibre of 3.7in. The 3.7in weapon was adopted in 1943 and soon proved to be an excellent equipment that was carried on a fixed mounting that could be moved with the aid of a special transporter. The details of this weapon included an L/65 barrel firing a 28lb (12.7kg) HE projectile with a muzzle velocity of 3,470ft (1,058m) per second, on-mounting elevation and traverse angles of 0 to +80 degrees and 360 degrees total respectively, and a maximum ceiling of 59,300ft (18,075m). The equipment was fitted with an automatic fuse setter and a power rammer, and remained in service into the later part of the 1950s, when it was replaced by guided missiles.

The Americans were convinced that their superb 0.5in (12.7mm) Browning M2HB heavy machine guns had the makings of a first-class multiple mounting for the engagement of low-flying tactical aircraft, and this resulted in the creation of their smallest-calibre anti-aircraft weapon as the Multiple Cal .50 Machine-gun Carriage M51. Designed by Maxson, this was a four-wheel trainer carrying four 0.5in machine guns in mountings powered electrically by batteries carried on the trainer, which was stabilised in firing position by four jacks. The machine guns, each supplied with 200 belted rounds of ammunition, were aimed with a US Navy Mk 9 reflector sight, and could be traversed and elevated very quickly to allow the successful engagement of high-speed targets with fast crossing speeds. The weight of the entire equipment was 2,396lb (1,087kg), and the cyclic rate of fire was 2,300 rounds per minute.

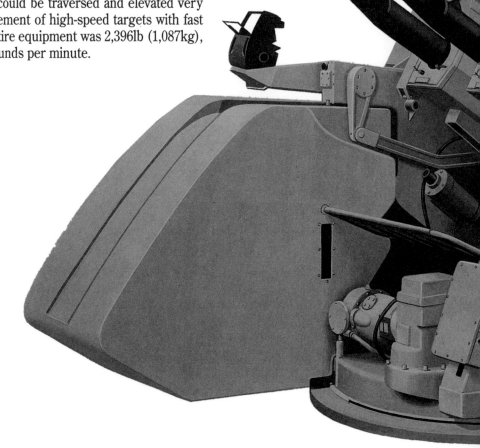

The Oerlikon GCM is typical of the modern generation of naval point-defence weapon systems for protection against low-level aircraft and missile attack. The mounting comes in three forms with open or enclosed accommodation for the single gunner, or alternatively, provision for remote control in an unmanned mounting, varying rates of traverse and elevation, and differing quantities of ammunition. Common to all is the potent armament of two 30mm KCB (originally Hispano-Suiza HS 831) cannon, firing a wide range of ammunition types at a high muzzle velocity for considerable range and accuracy

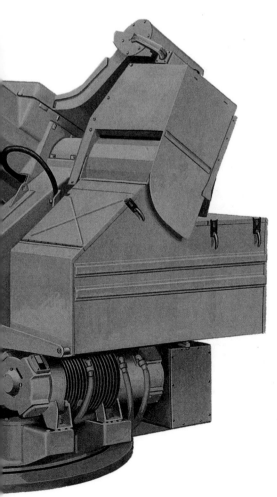

The Americans missed out the 20mm cannon for land-based applications, so their next anti-aircraft calibre was 37mm. Work on the ordnance was started in 1923 under the leadership of the celebrated John Browning, but ceased with his death in 1926 and was then resumed only in 1935 to create the 37mm Anti-aircraft Gun M1 that entered service in 1940 on the Carriage M3A1. This was a four-wheel unit whose wheels could be lifted to lower the mounting to the ground, where it was stabilised with the aid of two outrigger legs, and the ordnance could fire in single-short or automatic models using ammunition fed from the left in single rounds or from 10-round clips. Production totalled 7,278 equipments to a standard that included (in its M1A2 form on the M3A1 carriage) an L/53.7 barrel firing a 1.34lb (0.6kg) HE projectile with a muzzle velocity of 2,800ft (854m) per second, a weight of 6,124lb (2,778kg) in travelling order, on-mounting elevation and traverse angles of –5 to +90 degrees and 360 degrees total respectively, a cyclic rate of fire of 120 rounds per minute, and a maximum ceiling of 18,600ft (5,669m). The weapon was to have been replaced by the 40mm Anti-aircraft Gun M1 (the American licence-built version of the classic Swedish Bofors weapon), but supplies of this more advanced equipment never matched demand and production of the 37mm M1 was therefore continued. Experience showed that gunners tended to use tracer as a means of aiming the gun, and this expensive practice was therefore mitigated by combining the 37mm M1 gun with two 0.5in tracer-firing machine guns on the Combination Mount M54, which proved highly effective.

There was then a considerable calibre gap to the next size of American anti-aircraft gun, the 3in Anti-aircraft Gun M3 on Mount M2. This was the culmination of American use of the 3in calibre for anti-aircraft purposes from a time in World War I, and the M3 introduced a semi-automatic breech block as well as a large 'spider' firing platform stabilised by outriggers. The details of this weapon, which was obsolete by 1940 but used operationally in the Philippines during the Japanese invasion of those islands from December 1941, included an L/50 barrel firing a 12.8lb (5.8kg) HE projectile with a muzzle velocity of 2,800ft per second, a weight of 16,800lb (7,620kg) in travelling order, on-mounting elevation and traverse angles of –1 to +80 degrees and 360 degrees total respectively, and a maximum ceiling of 31,200ft (9,510m).

The successor to the 3in anti-aircraft gun in American service was the 90mm (3.54in) Anti-aircraft Gun M1 on Mount M1. Development of this weapon began in 1938, and the type was standardised for service in March 1940 as a highly effective if somewhat cumbersome weapon whose entry into service was delayed by the manufacturing complexity of the gun and the high precision of its fire-control system. The details of this weapon included an L/50 barrel firing a 23.4lb (10.6kg) HE projectile with a muzzle velocity of 2,700ft (823m) per second, a weight of 19,020lb (8,626kg) in travelling order, on-mounting elevation and traverse angles of 0 to +80 degrees and 360 degrees total respectively, and a maximum ceiling of 39,500ft (12,040m).

In July 1941 the US Army decided that its high-velocity anti-aircraft guns should also be capable of undertaking the anti-tank role in the fashion pioneered by the Germans with their 88mm weapons, and the immediate result was the Mount M2 to provide the 90mm Gun M1 with a genuinely mobile four-wheel carriage and a maximum depression angle. Design work began in September 1941 and the Mount M2 was standardised in May 1943 with a development of the 90mm Gun M1 as the Gun M2 with the M20 fuse setting and ramming system as well as a modified recoil system. Production of the 90mm Guns M1 and M2 lasted to August 1945 and totalled 7,831, and the details of the Gun M2 on mount M2 included an L/50 barrel firing a 23.4lb HE projectile with a muzzle velocity of 2,700ft per second, a weight of 32,300lb (14,651kg) in travelling order, on-mounting elevation and traverse angles of –10 to +80 degrees and 360 degrees total respectively, and a maximum ceiling of 39,500ft.

Of the American anti-aircraft guns used in World War II, that of largest calibre was the 120mm (4.72in) Anti-aircraft Gun M1 on Mount M1. The carriage had two axles with four twin-tyred wheels, and among the other features of this equipment, which was mostly retained in the USA for home defence, was two-piece ammunition loaded with the aid of a combined fuse setting and power ramming system. The details of this weapon included an L/60 barrel firing a 50lb (22.7kg) HE projectile with a muzzle velocity of 3,100ft (945m) per second, a weight of 61,500lb (27,896kg) in travelling order and 48,900lb (22,180kg) in firing position, on-mounting elevation and traverse angles of –5 to +80 degrees and 360 degrees total respectively, and a maximum ceiling of 56,000ft (17,070m).

The smallest calibre used by the Soviets for the dedicated anti-aircraft role was 25mm, and in this calibre there were three weapons, namely the 25mm Anti-Aircraft Gun Models 1939, 1940 and 1941. That made in the largest numbers, and of which the greatest amount is known, was the Model 1940 that appears to have been a development of a Bofors weapon that was carried on a carriage of four wheels that were raised as the mountings was stabilized in firing position by outriggers. The details of this weapon included an L/91.6 barrel fitted with a flash suppressor to fire an HE projectile of unrevealed weight with a muzzle velocity of 3,035ft (925m) per second, a weight of 2,370lb (1,075kg) in travelling order, on-mounting elevation and traverse angles of –10 to +85 degrees and 360 degrees total respectively, and a maximum ceiling of 15,010ft (4,575m).

Next up in calibre was the 37mm Anti-Aircraft Gun Model 1939, which appears to have been a reworking of the 40mm Bofors weapon revised to fire a clone of the 37mm Browning round from the USA. The equipment was based on a four-wheel carriage stabilized in firing position by outriggers carrying screw jacks, and among its other details was an L/74 barrel fitted with a flash suppressor to fire a 1.73lb (0.785kg) HE projectile with a muzzle velocity of 2,953ft (900m) per second, a weight of 4,630lb (2,100kg) in travelling order, on-mounting elevation and traverse angles of –5 to +85 degrees and 90 degrees total respectively, a rate of fire of 160 to 180 rounds per minute (cyclic) or 80 rounds per minute (practical), a maximum ceiling of 4,510ft (1,375m), and a crew of seven.

Complex, costly and beset by considerable teething problems, the 8.8cm FlaK 41 was the final member of Germany's 88mm (3.465in) series, and in service was a truly exceptional weapon offering magnificent anti-aircraft capability as well as a potent anti-tank facility that was seldom if ever used as the weapon was reserved for the defence of Germany's cities and industries.

Following this was the 76.2mm (3in) calibre, in which there were two equipments in the form of the Anti-Aircraft Gun Model 1931 and the Anti-Aircraft Gun Model 1938. The ordnances of the two equipments were basically similar, although a number of limited improvements was worked into that of the Model 38, so the primary differences lay in the equipments' carriages, which were a single-axle type for the Model 1931 and a two-axle type for the Model 1938. The details of the Model 1938 weapon included an L/55 barrel firing a 14.575lb (6.61kg) HE projectile with a muzzle velocity of 2,667ft (813m) per second, a weight of 9,283lb (4,210kg) in travelling order and 6,718lb (3,047kg) in firing position, on-mounting elevation and traverse angles of –3 to +82 degrees and 360 degrees total respectively, a maximum ceiling of 30,510ft (9,300m), and a crew of 11.

Another calibre used by the Soviets in the anti-aircraft role was 85mm (3.35in), and the two weapons in this calibre were the Anti-Aircraft Gun Model 1939 and Anti-Aircraft Gun 1944, alternatively known as the KS-12 and KS-18 respectively. Each of these equipments was carried on a two-axle carriage that was stabilized in firing position by four screw jacks, two of them on outrigger legs, and the details of the Model 1939 weapon included an L/55.2 barrel fitted with a multi-baffle muzzle brake to fire a 20.29lb (9.2kg) HE projectile with a muzzle velocity of 2,625ft (800m) per second, a weight of 9,305lb (4,220kg) in travelling order and 6,740lb (3,057kg) in firing position, on-mounting elevation and traverse angles of –2 to +82 degrees and 360 degrees total respectively, and a maximum ceiling of 34,450ft (10,500m). The Model 1944 was in essence an updated version of the Model 1939, and both weapons remained in service into the early 1980s.

The other two notable anti-aircraft guns used in World War II, and which also paved the way for their manufacturers' success with updated versions of these weapons as well as more advanced equipments since the end of World War II, were the 40mm Bofors gun from Sweden, and the 20mm Oerlikon cannon from Switzerland. Both weapons have been used in large numbers by a substantial number of countries, and were also made under licence by many nations for naval and land applications. The British Ordnance, QF, 40mm Bofors Mk I on Mounting Mk

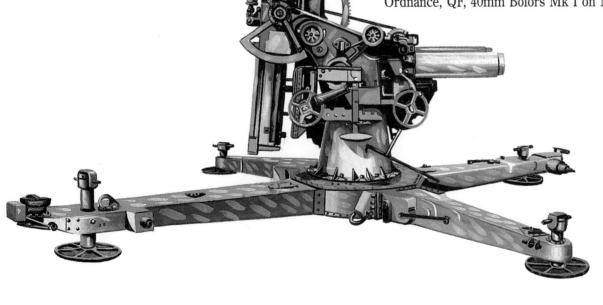

The FlaK 36 was, with the closely related FlaK 37, one of the two intermediate forms of the great family of German 88mm (3.465in) anti-aircraft guns that could also double with devastating capability in the anti-tank role.

73

III and Carriage Mk II, may be taken as typical of the type of Bofors guns used with such conspicuous success in World War II. The details of this weapon included an L/56 barrel fitted with a flash suppressor to fire a 1.96lb (0.89kg) HE projectile with a muzzle velocity of 2,800ft (853m) per second, a four-wheel carriage stabilised in firing position by four screw jacks (two of them on outriggers), a weight of 5,418lb (2,457kg) in travelling order, on-mounting elevation and traverse angles of –5 to +90 degrees and 360 degrees total respectively, a rate of fire of 120 rounds per minute (cyclic) or 60 to 90 rounds per minute (practical), a maximum ceiling of 23,600ft (7,195m), and a crew of five or six.

In the period after World War II, smaller-calibre anti-aircraft guns went out of favour with the exception of the 40mm Bofors weapon in its original L/56 and L/60 versions and later L/70 models, but then underwent a renaissance from the later 1950s as the medium- and high-altitude roles were assumed by guided missiles in place of the larger-calibre guns that had emerged from World War II and had been updated with a radar fire-control system. The smaller-calibre weapons were then seen to offer a capability against fixed-wing aircraft and, to an ever-increasing extent, rotary-wing machines that had come to exert a dominant effect on the land battlefield. Detailed below are some of the more important of these smaller-calibre weapons as well as a few medium-calibre weapons that were developed by the USSR and China.

The Czechoslovak 30mm M53 30mm is a twin anti-aircraft gun mounting with two L/81 barrels, a four-wheel carriage with outriggers but no shield, a weight of 4,630lb (2,100kg) in travelling order and 3,858lb (1,750kg) in firing position, on-mounting elevation and traverse angles of –10 to +85 degrees and 360 degrees total respectively, a rate of fire of 450 to 500 rounds per minute (cyclic) and 100 rounds per minute (practical) per barrel, and a horizontal range of 10,610yds (9,700m) maximum and a slant range of 3,280yds (3,000m) effective. This weapon entered service in the late 1950s, and offers considerable range advantages over Soviet towed 23mm equipments although it suffers from lack of radar fire-control, and is thus limited to clear-weather operation. Ammunition is fed by 10-round clips and the two basic ammunition types are HEI with a 0.99lb (0.45kg) projectile and AP-T with a 1.2lb (0.54kg) projectile able to pierce 55mm (2.16in) of armour at 545yds: both types are fired at a muzzle velocity of 3,281ft per second.

The French 20mm GIAT 76T2 Cerbère is a towed twin anti-aircraft gun mounting with two L/103.25 barrels, a two-wheel carriage with outriggers and a shield, a weight of 4,451lb (2,019kg) in travelling order and 3,336lb (1,513kg) in firing position, on-mounting elevation and traverse angles of –3.5 to +81.5 degrees in powered mode or –5 to +83 degrees in unpowered mode and 360 degrees total respectively, a rate of fire of 900 rounds per minute (cyclic) and 200 to 240 rounds per minute (practical) per barrel, a horizontal range of 6,560yds (6,000m) maximum and slant range of 2,185yds (2,000m) effective, and a crew of three. The equipment is a French development of the West German Rheinmetall MK 20 Rh 202 mounting with the original cannon replaced by two French GIAT M693 (F2) weapons. The type can be operated in the powered or manual modes, and there is a selectable dual-feed mechanism, ammunition supply amounting to 270 rounds per barrel. The Cerbère can be used with its on-mounting sight, or in conjunction with a radar fire-control system, or with a helmet-mounted target-indicator system.

Another French equipment, the 20mm GIAT 53T2 Tarasque is a towed twin anti-aircraft gun mounting with two L/103.25 barrels, a two-wheel carriage with outriggers and a shield, a weight of 1,852lb (840kg) in travelling order and 1,455lb (660kg) in firing position, on-mounting elevation and traverse angles of –8 to +83 degrees and 360 degrees total respectively, a rate of fire of 740 to 900 rounds per minute (cyclic) and 200 to 240 rounds per minute (practical), a horizontal range of 6,560yds maximum and slant range of 2,185yds effective, and a crew of three. Introduced in 1982, the Tarasque is a light anti-aircraft mounting (with secondary anti-AFV and anti-personnel capabilities) designed for rapid cross-country movement. The M693 (F2) weapon is hydraulically powered, and is dual-fed by belts for 100 HEI and 40 APDS rounds, the former having a muzzle velocity of 3,445ft (1,050m) per second and the latter of 4,242ft (1,293m) per second. The APDS projectile can penetrate 20mm (0.79in) of armour at a range of 1,095yds.

The German (formerly West German) 20mm Rheinmetall MK 20 Rh 202 is a towed twin anti-aircraft gun with two L/130.5 barrels, a two-wheel carriage with outriggers and a shield, a weight of 4,762lb (2,160kg) in travelling order and 3,616lb (1,640kg) in firing position, on-mounting elevation and traverse angles of –3.5 to +81.6 degrees in powered mode or –5.5 to +83.5 degrees in unpowered mode and 360 degrees total respectively, a rate of fire of 880 to 1,030 rounds per minute (cyclic) per barrel, a horizontal range of 3,280yds maximum and slant range of 2,185yds effective, and a crew of three or four. This twin-barrel light anti-aircraft equipment was produced to a West German specification, but has also been one of the most successful export weapons of its type as the designers found an excellent combination of accuracy (using a computerised optical sight), ammunition

Now obsolete as a result of its lack of armour and NBC protection, comparatively short range and limited fire-control system, the General Electric M163 was designed for battlefield protection of American mobile forces against air attack, and combined the M113 armoured personnel carrier with the M168 version of the General Electric Vulcan 20mm cannon, with a rotating assembly of six barrels to permit a rate of fire up to 3,000 rounds per minute. The type was used to devastating effect in the Vietnam War to break up infantry attacks and protect convoys against ambush.

One of the most powerful battlefield air-defence gun mountings currently in service, the Oerlikon-Bührle (now Oerlikon-Contraves) GDF combines two 35mm cannon on a powered mounting with any of several on-mounting computerised sight systems that can be cued with data from a higher-level source for earlier warning and other information.

supply and rates of traverse and elevation using an onboard power supply (a small petrol engine driving a hydraulic system). Each barrel has its own 270-round ammunition box, and there are another 10 rounds in the feed mechanism, the ammunition types being APDS-T, API-T, HEI and HEI-T fired at muzzle velocities of between 3,428 and 3,773ft (1,045 and 1,150m) per second.

The Israeli 20, 23 or 25mm RAMTA TCM Mk 3 is a towed twin anti-aircraft gun with two barrels whose length depends on the specific weapons installed, a two-wheel carriage with outriggers and a shield, a weight of 2,976lb (1,350kg) in towed configuration with 20mm Hispano-Suiza HS-404 cannon, on-mounting elevation and traverse angles of –6 to +85 in electrically powered mode or –10 to +90 degrees in manually operated mode and 360 degrees total respectively, a rate of fire of 700 rounds per minute (cyclic) and 150 rounds per minute (practical) per barrel with HS-404 cannon, a horizontal range of 6,235yds (5,700m) maximum and slant range of 1,315yds (1,200m) effective with HS-404 cannon, and a crew of three. This equipment entered service in 1984, and is essentially a product-improved TCM-20 with more modern assemblies (for greater reliability and less maintenance) plus a more advanced sight, the option of a night sight, and control by a computerised fire-control system with laser ranger. The same type of electric drive is used, and the accommodation of the weapons on special adaptors means that most types of 20, 23 and 25mm cannon can be installed. The mounting can also be fitted on the back of light armoured vehicles of the halftrack type still so favoured by the Israelis.

The Israeli 20mm RAMTA TCM-20 is a towed twin anti-aircraft gun with two barrels, a two-wheel carriage with outriggers and a shield, a weight of 2,976lb in travelling order with two loaded magazines, on-mounting elevation and traverse angles of –10 to +90 degrees and 360 degrees total respectively, a rate of fire of 700 rounds per minute (cyclic) and 150 rounds per minute (practical) per barrel, a horizontal range of 6,235yds maximum and slant range of 1,315yds effective, and a crew of three. Developed in Israel during the late 1960s, the TCM-20 is in essence an updated version of the US M55 mounting armed with two 20mm Hispano-Suiza HS-404 cannon rather than four 0.5in Browning M2HB heavy machine guns. The mounting is traversed and the weapon elevated by electric motors powered by two 12-volt batteries, the charge of the batteries being topped up by a small petrol engine. The type has built up an enviable combat record against low-flying aircraft, helicopters and light armoured vehicles, and can be installed on the back of vehicles such as the M2 and M3 halftracks. The two HS-404 cannon have been modified to use HS-804 ammunition (fed from 60-round drums) including APHE-T, APDS-T and HE-T. The type is optically controlled, but is often used with a radar warning system.

The 40mm Bofors 40L70 Type B is a towed anti-aircraft gun with an L/70 barrel, a four-wheel carriage with outriggers and a shield, a weight of 11,354lb (5,150kg) in travelling order, on-mounting elevation and traverse angles of –4 to +90 degrees and 360 degrees total respectively, a rate of fire of 240 or 300 rounds per minute (cyclic) in earlier and later models respectively, a horizontal range of 13,670yds (12,500m) maximum and slant range of 4,375yds (4,000m) effective, and a crew of four to six. The Bofors 40L70 Type A was introduced after World War II and remains one of the most powerful light weapons in the world (in both the surface-to-air and surface-to-surface roles) due to its high rate of fire (resulting from the use of an automatic breech and the ramming of each round during the run-out), good range and excellent ammunition. The Type A is the original model without on-carriage power, and weighs 10,582lb (4,800kg) in travelling order. The ammunition types are APC-T, HCHE, HE-T and PFHE fired at muzzle velocities of between 3,297 and 3,379ft (1,005 and 1,030m) per second, and the ammunition is fed in four-round clips into an optional overhead stay holding 26 rounds, and from two 48-round racks at the rear of

The ZRK Romb is a surface-to-air missile system for the short-range protection of mobile land formations, and is a self-contained equipment carried on a modified ZIL-167 6x6 truck chassis. The 'business' part of the system is carried on a turntable located on the upper decking, and comprises a single surveillance/target-acquisition radar and twin target-tracking/missile-guidance radars together with a bank of four SA-8 'Gecko' missiles delivered as certified rounds in sealed container/launchers. The system also includes an optical component (with a low-light-level TV camera) for continued capability when radar conditions have been degraded by physical conditions and/or the enemy's countermeasures.

Typifying the lowest end of the anti-aircraft capability spectrum, the ZPU-4 is a Russian equipment carrying four 14.5mm (0.57in) KPV heavy machine guns each supplied with ammunition from 150-round belts carried on the outside of the two banks of machine guns. Manually operated and optically aimed, the ZPU series was introduced in 1949 and is now obsolete in its single, twin and quadruple forms.

the carriage. The Bofors 40L70 Type B is an improved model with an on-carriage power generator, but otherwise similar to the Type A and operated in local control by a gunner on the left of the ordnance. The Bofors 40L70 BOFI Fair Weather is a development of the Type B with Bofors Optronic Fire-control Instrument (BOFI) and proximity-fused ammunition. This model weighs 12,125lb (5,500kg) in travelling order, and the BOFI equipment uses a laser rangefinder, a day/night image-intensifying sight and a fire-control computer to generate aiming and firing instructions for the gunner, with early warning provided optionally by an off-carriage radar system. The Bofors 40L70 BOFI All Weather is a development of the Bofors 40L70 BOFI Fair Weather system with the addition of a pulse-Doppler radar for automatic target acquisition and tracking capability. This model has a travelling weight of 12,556lb (5,700kg). The Breda 40L70 is the Bofors 40L70 built under licence in Italy, where Breda has developed an optional automatic feeding device, which takes ammunition in groups of three from a magazine pre-loaded with 144 rounds in four-round clips. The travelling weight of the Breda equipment is 11,684lb (5,300kg) and there are other detail differences in dimensions.

The Swiss 35mm Oerlikon GDF-005 is a towed twin anti-aircraft gun with two L/90 barrels, a four-wheel carriage with outriggers and a shield, a weight of 16,975lb (7,700kg) in travelling order with ammunition, on-mounting elevation and traverse angles of –5 to +92 degrees and 360 degrees total respectively, a rate of fire of 550 rounds per minute (cyclic) per barrel, a horizontal range of 10,390yds (9,500m) maximum and slant range of 4,375yds (4,000m) effective, and a crew of three. This is the most advanced model of a family of four twin 35mm anti-aircraft gun mountings that are the heavyweight members of Oerlikon's complement of anti-aircraft cannon. The GDF-001 was introduced in the early 1960s as the 2 ZLA 353 MK, and is an exceptionally potent weapon capable of effective use in the surface-to-air and surface-to-surface roles with its HEI, HEI-T and SAPHEI-T ammunition fired at a muzzle velocity of 3,855ft (1,175m) per second from the two KDB (formerly 353 MK) cannon, which are fed automatically from two 56-round containers replenished in seven-round clips from the two 63-round reserve containers on the carriage. The mounting has three operating modes, namely remote electric control from the Super Fledermaus or Skyguard fire-control radar, local electric control with the Xaba optical sight, and local manual control with handwheels. The GDF-002 is the updated version available from 1980 with Ferranti Type GSA Mk 3 sights and digital data transmission. The type is also available with optional packages such as camouflage, automatic reloaders, a gunner's cab, integrated power source, and a Minisight Gun King incorporating a laser rangefinder. The GDF-003 is the GDF-002 equipment built with the full upgrade package. The GDF-005 is the most modern version with a Gun King optronic sight system and, as standard, all the updating features available optionally on the earlier marks.

The Swiss 25mm Oerlikon GBI-A01 is a towed anti-aircraft gun with an L/80 barrel, a two-wheel carriage with tripod legs but no shield, a weight of 1,468lb (666kg) in travelling order and 1,116lb (506kg) in firing position, on-mounting elevation and traverse angles of –10 to +70 degrees and 360 degrees total respectively, a rate of fire of 570 rounds per minute (cyclic) and 170 rounds per minute (practical), a horizontal range of 6,560yds maximum and slant range of 2,735yds effective, and a crew of three. Although designed primarily for anti-aircraft use, the manually-operated GBI-A01 mounting can be used against battlefield targets such as light AFVs, the Oerlikon KBA-C cannon being able to fire APDS-T projectiles at a muzzle velocity of 4,380ft (1,335m) per second, plus HEI, HEI-T, SAPHEI and SAPHEI-T projectiles at 3,609ft (1,100m) per second. These rounds are accommodated in two 40-round containers (one on each side of the weapon), a dual-feed mechanism allowing selection of round type.

The Swiss 20mm Oerlikon GAI-D01 is a towed twin anti-aircraft gun with two L/95.3 barrels, a two-wheel carriage with outriggers and a shield, a weight of 3,968lb (1,800kg) in travelling order and 2,932lb (1,330kg) in firing position, on-mounting elevation and traverse angles of –3 to +81 degrees in powered mode or –5 to +85 degrees in manually operated mode and 360 degrees total respectively, a rate of fire of 1,000 rounds per minute (cyclic) per barrel, a horizontal range of 6,235yds maximum and slant range of 1,640yds effective, and a crew of five. Designed in the mid-1970s as the Hispano-Suiza HS-666A and available from 1978, this equipment has successfully bridged the tactical gap between Oerlikon's single-barrel 20mm weapons and more capable equipments such as the twin-barrel 35mm GDF-002. The equipment is hydraulically powered, with reversion to manual operation in emergencies, and although intended primarily for anti-aircraft use can also be deployed for a number of battlefield roles. The two KAD-B cannon can fire AP-T, HEI, HEI-T, SAPHEI and SAPHEI-T ammunition (the first at a muzzle

The Chinese Type 59 towed anti-aircraft gun mounting is a copy of the Soviet 57mm S-60 equipment, and is wholly obsolete in the anti-aircraft role as a result of its optical sighting and poor rates of electrically powered elevation and traverse. The details of this equipment include an L/77 barrel with a muzzle brake, length of 28ft 2.65in (8.60m), weight of 10,538lb (4,780kg), elevation arc of between –5 and +87 degrees, traverse of 360 degrees, rate of fire of 100-120 rounds per minute (cyclic), muzzle velocity of 3,281ft (1,000m) per second to loft its HE projectile to a horizontal range of 13,125yds (12,000m) maximum and slant range of 6,560yds (6,000m) effective, and detachment of seven or eight.

velocity of 4,380ft (1,335m) per second, plus HEI, HEI-T, SAPHEI and SAPHEI-T projectiles at 3,609ft (1,100m) per second. These rounds are accommodated in two 40-round containers (one on each side of the weapon), a dual-feed mechanism allowing selection of round type.

The Swiss 20mm Oerlikon GAI-C04 is a towed anti-aircraft gun typical of the manufacturer's single-barrel equipments, and its details include an L/95.3 barrel, a two-wheel carriage with tripod legs but no shield, a weight of 1,299lb (589kg) in travelling order and 959lb (435kg) in firing position, on-mounting elevation and traverse angles of –7 to +83 degrees and 360 degrees total respectively, a rate of fire of 1,050 rounds per minute (cyclic), a horizontal range of 6,235yds maximum and slant range of 1,640yds effective, and a crew of three. Developed as the Hispano-Suiza HS-639-B3.1 and fitted with a KAD-B13-3 (formerly HS-820-SL7 A3-3) cannon, the baseline GAI-C01 is a manually operated equipment with weights (in travelling order and in firing position respectively, each with ammunition) of 1,177 and 816lb (534 and 370kg). The type fires the same ammunition as the GAI-D01, and is single-fed by a 75-round magazine on the right of the weapon, so limiting the type's

Above: This is the Chinese-built copy of the Soviet (now Russian) ZU-23-2 light towed anti-aircraft equipment with an armament of a side-by-side pair of 23mm cannon firing API or HEI rounds with a muzzle velocity of 3,182ft (970m) per second. The ammunition is carried in 50-round belts in boxes outside each weapon, and the equipment is designed only for clear-weather operations as it lacks anything but a simple optical sight, and its capabilities are further degraded in the anti-aircraft role by the fact that it is manually operated and therefore lacks the fast elevation and traverse rates to deal with modern high-performance aircraft.

Left: Based on the hull and automotive system of the Type 69-II main battle tank, the Chinese Type 80 self-propelled anti-aircraft gun system offers excellent mobility and good protection in its primary task of providing battlefield air defence for armoured formations but, like the Soviet (now Russian) ZSU-57-2 on which it was based, it has a distinctly limited simple optical sighting system. The turret-mounted armament comprises two 57mm Type 59 guns, each supplied with 300 rounds of 14.26lb (6.47kg) HE and 14.22lb (6.45kg) APC ammunition,.

utility in dual-role operations. The GAI-C03 was developed as the HS-639-B4.1 and is fitted with a KAD-A01 (formerly HS-820) anti-aircraft cannon. This equipment fires the same ammunition as the GAI-D01, although rounds are fed to the cannon from an overhead drum containing 50 rounds. The type has weights (in travelling order and in firing position respectively, complete with ammunition) of 1,124 and 952lb (510 and 432kg). The GAI-C04 was developed as the HS-639-B5 and is fitted with a KAD-B14 (formerly HS-820-SL7 A4) cannon. This is therefore an improved version of the GAI-C01 with a dual-feed mechanism and two 75-round magazines for greater capability in the surface-to-air and secondary surface-to-surface roles.

The Soviet 57mm S-60 is a towed anti-aircraft gun with an L/77 barrel with a 'pepperpot' muzzle brake, a four-wheel carriage with outriggers but no shield, a weight of 10,273lb (4,660kg) in travelling order and 9,921lb (4,500kg) in firing position, on-mounting elevation and traverse angles of –4 to +85 degrees and 360 degrees total respectively, a rate of fire of 110 rounds per minute (cyclic) and 70 rounds per minute (practical), a horizontal range of 13,125yds (12,000m) maximum and slant range of 4,375yds (4,000m) with on-carriage control or 6,560yds (6,000m) with off-carriage control, and a crew of seven. The S-60 was introduced in the late 1940s as a heavy tactical anti-aircraft weapon to replace the 37mm Model 1939. The equipment fires FRAG and APC ammunition (of the fixed type and fed in four-round clips) at a muzzle velocity of 3,281ft per second. Although it can be used with its on-carriage fire-control system, it is far more capable when used with 'Fire Can' or 'Flap Wheel' radar and appropriate director. Night vision sights have also been seen on the type, which can be operated manually or with servo-assistance.

The American 20mm General Electric (now Martin Marietta) M167 Vulcan is a multi-barrel towed anti-aircraft gun with an assembly of six L/76.2 barrels, a two-wheel carriage with outriggers but no shield, a weight of 3,500lb (1,588kg) in travelling order and 3,450lb (1,565kg) in firing

Known in the West as the ZSU-30-4 but in Russia as the 2S6 Tunguska, this is an extremely capable anti-aircraft system for the protection of important battlefield formations. The type is based on the fully tracked hull of the MT-S tracked command vehicle, carrying a fully traversing turret fitted with two types of armament (two 30mm cannon and eight SA-19 surface-to-air missiles) together with the advanced 'Hot Shot' fire-control system with surveillance radar, tracking radar and an optronic sight.

position, on-mounting elevation and traverse angles of –5 to +80 degrees and 360 degrees total respectively, a rate of fire selectable between 1,000 (surface-to-surface) or 3,000 (surface-to-air) rounds per minute, a horizontal range of 6,500yds (5,945m) maximum and slant range of 1,300yds (1,190m) effective, and a crew of one. The M167 is the towed version of the M163 self-propelled anti-aircraft gun, and although it features a capable fire-control system (with range-only radar and a lead-computing sight) and the formidable Vulcan six-barrel cannon plus 500 rounds of ammunition (AP and HEI fired at a muzzle velocity of 3,380ft/1,030m per second), the equipment is limited by the absence of external power and its lack of all-weather capability. The type has been improved in reliability and cross-country mobility by the addition of an extra wheel on each side.

Right: The Gepard is still one of the most powerful battlefield air defence systems available, and is a German and Swiss development with two extremely powerful 35mm cannon on the sides of a turret accommodating a highly capable radar-directed fire-control system and installed on the tracked chassis of the Leopard 1 main battle tank.

Below: The ZSU-57-2 is the Soviet original from which the Chine Type 80 was developed, and is a large and slow-traversing turret with two 57mm S-60 guns on the hull of the T-54 main battle tank.

Descended directly from the Bofors 40mm anti-aircraft guns of World War II, the Bofors 40L70 40mm gun is still an exceptional weapon for use against low-flying aircraft and lighter battlefield vehicles, as a result of its high performance with thoroughly modern ammunition and the fact that it can be fitted with an advanced sight system updatable from higher-level radars.

The Guided Missile

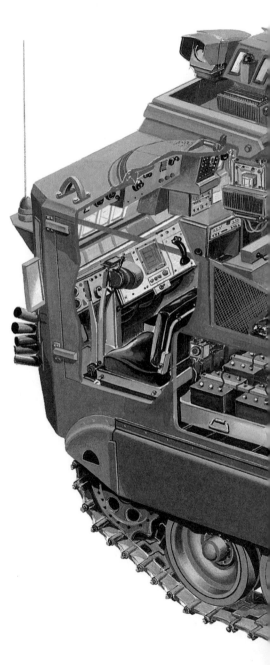

Throughout the greatest part of its history, right up to the period following World War II, two of the primary problems with artillery were inability to engage targets at very short range, and its relative lack of accuracy at longer ranges: these two factors combined to reduce the overall military utility of heavy artillery, and to make the destruction of long-range targets expensive in terms of the number of rounds of ammunition that had to be fired before the target had been destroyed. For these reasons, therefore, a desire was often expressed for the creation of a weapon that offered greater accuracy than artillery for the probability of the destruction of specific targets at long range.

The first practical expression of this desire was the 'locomotive' torpedo brought to a practical level by Robert Whitehead in 1868. This may truly claim to be the precursor of the modern guided missile, for it combined moderately long range and considerable destructive power in a single weapon made significantly more accurate than any of its predecessors by an onboard guidance package comprising a gyroscopic platform for course-keeping and any one of several depth-keeping systems for control of the weapon's running depth under the water. By the end of the nineteenth century, the torpedo had been brought to a high state of capability for launch firstly by surface ships and later by submarines, and then during the course of World War I by the aeroplane.

In its basic form, the torpedo had no terminal guidance system, for there were no cybernetic systems on which any real form of terminal guidance could have been based. Before it was fired, the weapon therefore relied on the insertion of the parameters of its own launch position and the expected interception point.

The same basic concept was used in the first aerial guided missile to reach the hardware stage after design as a surface-to-surface bombardment weapon. This was the Delco/Sperry Bug designed in 1917 for the US Army as a small aeroplane-type weapon that was capable of delivering a 300lb (136kg) warload over a range of some 62 miles (100km) with a fair degree of accuracy, as a result of its guidance by a Sperry system using an altimeter for longitudinal control, a primitive gyroscopic platform for lateral and directional control, and an engine revolution counter for range control. The 'missile' was a small biplane made of wood-reinforced papier maché with a card skin, and was powered by a 40hp (29.8kW) Ford petrol engine. Plans were laid for the type's mass production as a bombardment weapon for use on the Western Front, but the Armistice of November 1918 ended hostilities before the type could be placed in large-scale production.

A number of experimental types, designed to achieve the same basic function of surface-to-surface bombardment and also a limited surface-to-air capability against German airships, were built in the UK under the cover designation Aerial Target by a team under the supervision of Professor A.M. Low at the RFC Experimental Works and then the Royal Aircraft Factory at

Farnborough. These types lacked the gyroscopic control system and were therefore designed for command guidance by radio.

Germany undertook the experimental development of remotely piloted glide bombs in the course of World War I. Resulting from an initiative of Dr Wilhelm von Siemens of the Siemens-Schuckert Werke, these SSW types were tested in 1915 as glide bombs with guidance commands transmitted to the control surfaces (powered by an onboard battery), via fine copper wires that were unreeled as the weapon departed from its launch aeroplane. The concept was fully and successfully evaluated in a number of monoplane and biplane test models, but plans to use such glide bombs were overtaken by Germany's defeat.

Other such types were mooted in the 1920s and early 1930s by far-sighted designers, but foundered on a dearth of military enthusiasm for such weapons at a time of straitened finances, and on the lack of a powerplant

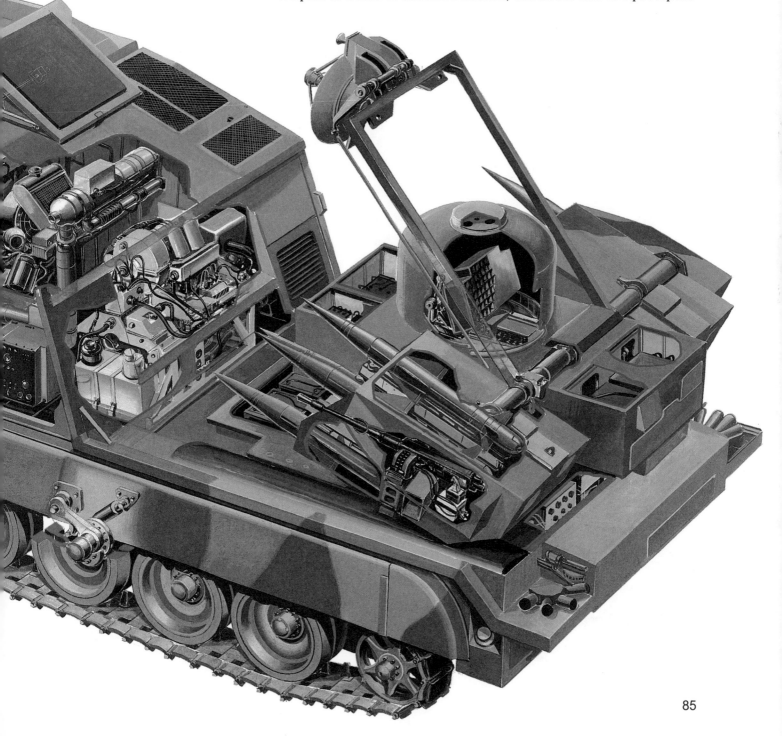

Based on the hull of the M113 armoured personnel carrier, the BAe Tracked Rapier is one of the world's best short-range surface-to-air missile systems, and carries eight Rapier 'hittiles' (missiles so accurate that they generally hit the target directly and therefore carry only a vestigial explosive warhead) together with the surveillance radar, optronic sight and microwave missile guidance link.

The first ballistic missile to enter service anywhere in the world, the Peenemünde A-4 is better known by its Nazi designation of V-2, and was used in moderately large numbers during the closing stage of World War II as the Germans tried to terrorise the British into surrender.

other than the piston engine whose use would result in a weapon that was not appreciably faster than current warplanes and was therefore comparatively simple to intercept and shoot down. The turning point in the concept of the guided missile, from being a feasible but not necessarily practical or desirable weapon, came in the mid-1930s with the rise to power in Germany of the Nazi party and the first development of effective reaction-type engines such as the turbojet, pulsejet and rocket motor. The German military at last began to appreciate that unmanned but guided weapons using such reaction motors offered hitherto unrealisable performance, and the leaders of the Nazi party saw the opportunity not only to redress the overall weight of the military balance in favour of Germany – which was denied the right to develop advanced weapons during the currency of the Treaty of Versailles that had signalled Germany's defeat in World War I – but also to overtake Germany's potential enemies through the mass production of weapons that resulted from the German 'genius'.

A major development effort was started in the later 1930s and during the first years of World War II, and from 1942 was progressed as a matter of high priority as Germany's conventional forces were checked for the first time in the nation's aggressive quest for territorial and political expansion, and particularly as the Allied powers began to drive the German forces back towards Germany.

The German research and development effort had strategic as well as tactical ambitions, the two strategic weapons to enter large-scale service being the Fieseler Fi 103 flying bomb or cruise missile, and the Peenemünde A-4 ballistic missile.

The first guided missile to be used operationally in large numbers, the Fi 103 was a pilotless flying bomb for the bombardment of large urban areas. Development of the weapon was authorised in June 1942, and the Fi 103 began to take shape under the leadership of Dipl.-Ing. Robert Lusser as an aeroplane-shaped weapon with a circular-section fuselage carrying, from nose to tail, the master magnetic compass, the warhead, the fuel tank, the two high-pressure air tanks used to power the control surfaces and feed the fuel to the engine, the battery, the master gyro assembly and guidance package, and the pneumatic servos controlling the elevators and rudder. The rest of the airframe comprised the flying surfaces, which included the cantilever mid-set wing and a plain tail unit whose vertical surface provided the rear support for the pulsejet engine whose forward end was carried by a pylon over the battery section.

The first unpowered test vehicle was launched from a Focke-Wulf Fw 200 Condor motherplane in December 1942, and the first powered ground launch took place later in the same month. There were a number of development problems, but the weapon was ready for use in the summer of 1944 after some 300 Fi 103s had been fired in trials. The weapon was dubbed V-1 (Vergeltungswaffe-1, or reprisal weapon-1) by the Nazi party, and the first was fired against London on 12 June 1944.

The offensive that followed saw the launch by the Luftwaffe of 8,617 standard missiles against London and other British targets in the period up to the end of August 1944, when the programme was taken over by the German army, which fired 11,988 weapons against a range of European targets in the period up to the end of March 1945. Another version of the weapon had wooden wings and a smaller warhead for longer-range attacks, and 275 of these weapons were fired by the SS against British targets between January and March 1945. Finally, the Luftwaffe fired 865 missiles from adapted Heinkel He 111 bombers between September 1944 and March 1945.

Generally known by its Nazi designation V-2 (Vergeltungswaffe-2, or reprisal weapon-2), the A-4 weapon was in every respect a prodigious

The SD-1400 X, otherwise known as the 'Fritz-X', was the first guided weapon to achieve a major success, for it was a weapon of this guided glide bomb type that was used to sink the Italian battleship *Roma* in September 1943. The weapon was basically a heavy armour-piercing bomb fitted with wings and a tail unit, the latter carrying the spoiler-type controls that were activated via a radio link from the operator in the launch aeroplane.

achievement for its period, and marked the emergence of the ballistic missile as a new type of weapon for strategic purposes. The unsuccessful first launch was attempted in June 1942, the successful second launch following in August. There were considerable development difficulties with the missile, and no fewer than 265 test launches were made before the type entered service. The weapon was based on a tapered circular-section body carrying, from top to bottom, the warhead, the guidance package of gyroscopes and integrating accelerometers, the tank for 8,311lb (3,770kg) of alcohol fuel, the tank for 10,802lb (4,900kg) of liquid oxygen oxidant, the fuel and oxidant turbopumps powered by hydrogen peroxide and calcium permanganate, and the rocket motor. Round the base of the missile was a cruciform of swept fins each carrying a control surface, and four graphite vanes were fitted in the exhaust to control the missile by vectoring the thrust of its engine before the weapon had reached a speed at which the aerodynamic control surfaces became effective. The first A-4 was fired operationally on 8 September 1944, and in a programme that lasted to 27 March 1945, a total of 3,165 A-4s was fired against British and European targets.

The Germans also expended considerable but not altogether successful effort in the creation of a number of tactical missiles of the air-to-air, surface-to-air and air-to-surface types. It was only weapons of the last category that reached operational service, and then only in limited numbers and mainly for the anti-ship role. The two most important of these weapons were the Ruhrstahl SD-1400 X and Henschel Hs 293. Otherwise known as the X-1, Fritz-X or FX-1400, the SD-1400 X was designed by Max Kramer for a first test launch in 1942, and scored its greatest success on 9 September 1943 when two such weapons hit and sank the Italian battleship *Roma* as she was steaming to Malta after the Italian armistice with the Allies: each weapon was a guided version of the SD-1400 armour-piercing bomb with an arrangement of four fixed wings on the centre of gravity and a lengthened tail section carrying an ovoid ring tail embodying spoiler controls that moved under control of the operator in the launch warplane. This weapon was fully practical in the technical and operational senses, but only about 100 of the type were used in real missions because of losses to the launch warplanes, which were heavily laden and vulnerable when flying to the target area, and then slow and vulnerable as they cruised in the target area during the attack, for which the operator used the standard Lofte 7 bombsight as the pilot flew straight and level until weapon impact. A variant with Telefunken FuG 208/238 wire command guidance did not enter service.

The Germans displayed a keen interest in the development of stand-off weapons even before the outbreak of World War II, and one of the first fruits of this enthusiasm was the Hs 293A air-to-surface missile designed under the leadership of Herbert Wagner. The core of the weapon was a standard 551lb (250kg) SC-250 bomb to which were added a mid-set wing of the constant-chord type with inset ailerons and also a cumbersome tail unit that was designed to accommodate the autopilot and guidance package (not yet available) as well as the horizontal tail surface, the deep ventral portion that stabilized the missile in the directional plane even though there was no rudder, and the large flare that facilitated optical tracking of the missile by its operator. It was in this form as a glide bomb that the weapon was first tested, but then a powerplant was added in the form of a Walter liquid-propellant rocket extended below the body of the weapon on short struts and exhausting obliquely downward and to the rear.

The first warplane selected as launch type for the Hs 293A initial production model was the Dornier Do 217E bomber, and the relevant aircraft were modified with an operator position in the starboard side of the forward crew compartment. This meant that the Hs 293A had to be released as the launch warplane paralleled the course of the target off to its right, and that the pilot had to hold a steady course as the operator kept the flare on the tail of the missile superimposed over the target image until impact. The Hs 293A was used operationally over the Mediterranean, Atlantic Ocean and North Sea (its first success was the sinking of the British sloop *Egret* on 25 August 1943 in the Bay of Biscay), and a number of the missiles were also expended in attempts to destroy the bridges being used by the Soviets to cross the Rivers Vistula and Oder in the spring of 1945.

Variants of the Hs 293 series that proceeded no further than the prototype or project stage were the Hs 293B with the Staru FuG 207/237 wire-guidance system; the Hs 293C intended to penetrate under the surface of the sea before hitting the underside of a target ship's hull; the Hs 293D with Fernseh TV guidance; the Hs 293E with spoiler controls; the Hs 293F proposed tailless model; and the He 293H with the Schmidding 109-503 or Schmidding 109-512 rocket motor for carriage by the Arado Ar 234 Blitz jet-powered bomber.

Another essentially simple but nonetheless far-sighted weapon developed in Germany during World War II, the Henschel Hs 293 was an air-to-surface missile with flying surfaces for extended range, rocket propulsion for moderately high performance, and radio for command guidance.

The type of tactical missile into which the greatest effort went was the surface-to-air type, for it was with such weapons that the Germans thought they could stem and possibly even defeat the Allied bombing effort that was destroying Germany's urban areas, communication arteries, and industrial capacity.

Although none of them entered service, the most important of these weapons were the Henschel Hs 117 Schmetterling (butterfly), Messerschmitt Enzian (gentian), Peenemünde Wasserfall (waterfall) and Rheinmetall Rheintochter (Rhine daughter). The Hs 117 was the German surface-to-air missile that came closest to operational service, and had its origins in the Hs 297 design study undertaken by Professor Wagner in 1941. The weapon was based on an aeroplane-shaped structure that was boosted by two strap-on solid-propellant rockets that fell away after exhausting their propellant, leaving the missile to fly the rest of its mission on its liquid-propellant sustainer. The operator had to have a clear line of sight to the target (although radar guidance was later incorporated into the system), and steered the missile via a radio command system. Trials began in May 1944, and full production was authorised in December 1944, the first weapon being on the verge of service when Germany surrendered in May 1945.

The Enzian was a ramp-launched surface-to-air missile based on the aerodynamics of the Me 163 Komet rocket-powered point interceptor, and was controlled by elevons responding to operator commands via a radio link. Some 38 test missiles were fired with varying degrees of success before the programme was cancelled in January 1945.

The Wasserfall was one of the most advanced surface-to-air missiles developed in Germany during World War II and was a supersonic weapon based on the aerodynamics of the A-4 (V-2) ballistic missile with a cruciform of small mid-set wings. The guidance system was notably complex and caused many problems with the development of this potentially excellent weapon, and the programme was further delayed by design modifications. The first attempt at a test launch in January 1944 ended with the explosion of the missile on its pad, but the second launch attempt was successful in the following month. Some 35 missiles had been launched in the development programme before Peenemünde was evacuated during February 1945 in the face of a Soviet advance.

The Rheintochter was an ambitious two-stage surface-to-air missile based on an extremely powerful booster stage with four swept and braced fins, and

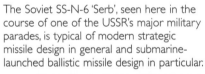

The Soviet SS-N-6 'Serb', seen here in the course of one of the USSR's major military parades, is typical of modern strategic missile design in general and submarine-launched ballistic missile design in particular.

a less powerful sustainer stage with a cylindrical body carrying six swept wings at its rear and a cruciform of all-moving control surfaces at its nose. The first Rheintochter I missile was fired from a converted 88mm (3.465in) anti-aircraft gun mounting in August 1943, and used command-to-line-of-sight guidance. The Rheintochter I programme was abandoned in December 1944 after the firing of 82 missiles and was replaced by the Rheintochter III with laterally mounted booster rockets. This programme was abandoned after the firing of a few development missiles.

In the air-to-air category, Germany developed two missiles as the Henschel Hs 298 and Ruhrstahl X-4. The Hs 298 was the world's first air-to-air missile to reach the hardware stage before the programme was terminated in December 1944, and was an aeroplane-configured weapon with an oval-section pod-and-boom body, slightly swept wings and a tail unit with underslung endplate vertical surfaces outboard of the efflux of the rocket motor installed in the lower part of the pod to exhaust under the boom. Guidance was provided by a radio command system. The most advanced missile developed by the Germans in World War II was the Kramer-designed X-4 that was based on a circular-section body tapered fore and aft of the cruciform of swept wooden wings. Propulsion was entrusted to a liquid-propellant rocket motor exhausting through a nozzle inside the small cruciform of tail-mounted fins each carrying a control surface, and guidance was provided by commands transmitted to the missile from an

The first major type of submarine-launched ballistic missile (SLBM) developed in the USSR was the SS-N-8 'Sawfly' designed for carriage in the 'Yankee' class of submarines, which each possessed two side-by-side rows of eight missile tubes abaft the sail.

Although much discussed at the time of its first appearance in the mid-1960s, the SS-10 'Scrag' did not enter Soviet service but was important in the development of the SS-18 intercontinental ballistic missile (ICBM).

Early surface-to-air missiles, especially those intended for the high-altitude interception of strategic bombers, tended to be large and also required a significant technical infrastructure as well as major radar installations for target acquisition and tracking and then missile guidance. Typical of such missiles are two American types, the Nike Ajax (elevated) and Nike Hercules (flat).

operator in the launch aeroplane via two copper wires unwound from bobbins at the tips of two opposing wings on the missile.

The effect of these German weapons was immense, and the victorious Allies made every effort to seize German missile development centres with all their research and design data, and also to secure the services of German missile designers and engineers. The two most successful of the Allies in the garnering of this advantage were inevitably the USSR and the USA, and this gave the two countries an immense boost in the development of such weapons during the late 1940s and early 1950s. Both countries had been involved in missile development to a limited degree during World War II, but the only missile to emerge as an operational type was an American air-to-surface weapon, the ASM-N-2 Bat designed to provide the Consolidated PB4Y Privateer with a potent anti-ship capability as well as the ability to destroy point targets such as bridges. A few examples of this unpowered glide bomb type were used successfully in 1945: the weapon was based on an aeroplane-type airframe with a high-set wing and a low-set tail unit whose horizontal surface carried endplate vertical surfaces, and four slipstream-driven generators supplied electrical power for the weapon's systems and for the control package, which was based on an autopilot supplemented by Western Electric semi-active radar for the terminal phase of the flight.

Development of missiles in versatility and overall capability since the end of World War II has resulted in the guided missiles that are now widely employed in the primary surface-to-surface (land strategic, land tactical, sea strategic and sea tactical), air-to-surface (strategic and tactical), and surface-to-air roles. Below are discussed a number of the more important weapons in these categories, listed by country of origin in alphabetical order.

Designated CSS-1 in the US terminology for Chinese weapons, the Dong Feng-2 (East Wind-2) is a simple single-stage medium-range ballistic weapon that was China's first strategic missile and introduced in 1970. It is based on the technology of the Soviet SS-3 'Shyster', itself based generally on the German A-4 (V-2) of World War II. The type remains in Chinese service (some 50 such weapons), but has only very limited value with details that include a length of 74ft 9.6in (22.80m), weight of 57,319lb (26,000kg), propulsion by one liquid-propellant rocket, range of 746 miles (1,200km), CEP of 3,040yds (2,780m), warhead of one 15/20-kiloton nuclear or conventional RV in early examples or 1/3-megaton thermonuclear RV in later examples, radio-updated inertial guidance, and hot launch from a fixed pad.

The Dong Feng-3, otherwise known as the CSS-2, is another single-stage intermediate-range ballistic missile (IRBM) whose details include a length of 67ft 7in (20.60m), weight of 59,524lb (27,000kg), propulsion by one storable liquid-propellant rocket, range of 1,988 miles (3,200km), CEP of 1,520yds (1,390m), warhead of one ⅓megaton thermonuclear RV in early examples or three 100-kiloton nuclear multiple independently targeted re-entry vehicles (Mirvs) in later examples, radio-updated inertial guidance, and hot launch from a fixed pad. The DF-3 was introduced in 1971, and is based on Soviet technology using storable hypergolic propellants. Some 60 such missiles are in service, and an alternative estimate puts range at 1,680 miles (2,700km) with the megaton-class single warhead. The improved variant with Mirved warhead was first tested in 1986, and is a two-stage weapon. In 1988, China supplied some 60 modified DF-3s to Saudi Arabia, and these are of the DF-3A variant with an increased payload in the form of a large conventional warhead. The maximum payload is thought to by 4,510lb (2,045kg) of HE carried over a range of 1,680 miles.

The Dong Feng-4 (CSS-3) is a two-stage limited-range intercontinental ballistic missile (ICBM) whose details include a length of 87ft 11in (26.80m), weight of 110,229lb (50,000kg), propulsion by single storable liquid-propellant rockets in each stage, range of 4,350 miles (7,000km), CEP of 1,017yds (930m), warhead of one 2-megaton thermonuclear RV, inertial guidance, and hot launch from a silo. The DF-4 was introduced in 1978 and only a few such missiles remain in service. The type also forms the basis for the CZ-1 (Long March-1) series of satellite-launch vehicles.

The Dong Feng-5 (CSS-4) is a two-stage ICBM whose details include a length of 141ft 10.75in (43.25m), weight of 445,326lb (202,000kg) including a 3,086lb (1,400kg) payload bus, propulsion by four storable liquid-propellant rockets each delivering 154,321lb st (686.45kN) in the first stage and one storable liquid-propellant rocket in the second stage, range of 6,214 miles (10,000km), CEP of 1,017yds (930m), warhead of one 4-megaton thermonuclear RV, inertial guidance, and hot launch from a silo. The DF-5 entered limited service in 1981, and has also been developed into the CZ-2 (Long March-2) two-stage and CZ-3 (Long March-3) three-stage satellite launchers. The Dong Feng-6, also known in the West as the CSS-4, is an improved version of the DF-5 but able to carry a 5-megaton thermonuclear warhead over a range of 8,078 miles (13,000km) and believed to be the genuine production version of the type.

The Dong Feng-7 (CSS-5) is a three-stage ICBM of which very little is known other than the fact that it carries up to 10 kiloton-range Mirved warheads, has inertial guidance and is hot launched from a silo. The DF-7 is China's latest and most capable ICBM with an advanced type of warhead, and its whole launch system is based on that of the CZ-3 satellite launcher, itself derived from the DF-4 ICBM.

Carried here by a vehicle based on the hull of the PT-76 light tank, the FROG series of unguided rockets were designed to provide long-range bombardment capability with nuclear, chemical or conventional warheads.

The American MGM-31 Pershing II was an operational-level surface-to-surface missile so accurate that it could be fitted with a very small nuclear warhead, as this was more than adequate to ensure the destruction of a target after almost pinpoint arrival.

The Aérospatiale SSBS S-3D is a French two-stage IRBM whose details include a length of 45ft 3.33in (13.80m), weight of 56,878lb (25,800kg), propulsion by one SEP 902 Herisson (P16) solid-propellant rocket delivering 121,252lb st (539.35kN) for 76 seconds in the first stage and one SEP Rita II (P6) solid-propellant rocket delivering 70,547lb st (313.81kN) for 52 seconds in the second stage, range of 1,864 miles (3,000km), CEP of 908yds (830m), warhead of one 1.2-megaton thermonuclear RV with penetration aids, Sagem/EMD inertial guidance, and hot launch from a silo. Designed as a successor to the SSBS S-2 during the 1970s, the SSBS S-3D mounts a higher-performance second stage on the first stage of the S-2, and entered service in 1980 in France's 18 IRBM silos. The improved TN-61 warhead is hardened against high-altitude nuclear explosions, and carries a new generation of penetration aids. Some estimates put the range as high as 2,175 miles (3,500km), and the weapon is to be phased out of service in the late 1990s as France concentrates its nuclear deterrent capability in its missile-launching submarines.

Israel is extremely reluctant to divulge any details of the country's ballistic missile programme, and indeed the first overt public information about such developments came only in July 1986, when the USSR warned Israel against the continued development of such weapons. It is thought that the programme began in the early 1960s, resulting in the Jericho I development weapon, produced with considerable technical aid from the French and capable of a range of between 280 and 404 miles (450 and 650km) with a 1,102lb (500kg) warhead, probably of the HE type although suggestions of a nuclear type should not be discounted. After the Franco-Israeli split of 1967, the programme was advanced by Israel and, from 1977, with financial support from Iran, resulted in the Jericho IIA, otherwise known as the Shavit and the basis of a surface-to-surface missile test-fired by South Africa in 1989. The Israeli weapon is now operational, and is probably

Seen here in the course of a test launch, the MSBS M-4 is one of the French navy's more important SLBMs.

based in the Negev desert close to the Dimona facility at which Israel's nuclear weapons are manufactured. The Jericho IIA is reported to possess a range of 932 miles (1,500km) and to carry a nuclear warhead, although test flights have revealed a possible range of 510 miles (820km) with a larger 1,653lb (750kg) conventional warhead. In the late 1980s it was thought that the Israelis had an improved Jericho IIB version under development, probably to carry a heavier warload over the same basic range.

The SS-4 'Sandal' was a Soviet single-stage medium-range ballistic missile whose details included a length of 74ft 8.5in (22.77m), weight of 59,524lb (27,000kg) with a 2,976lb (1,350kg) payload bus, propulsion by one liquid-propellant rocket, range of 1,243 miles (2,000km), CEP of 2,625yds (2,400m), warhead of one 1-megaton thermonuclear or HE RV, inertial guidance, and hot launch from a pad with reload capability when fired from unhardened sites. A development of the SS-3 'Shyster', the SS-4 entered service in 1958 and was later phased out in favour of the SS-20.

The SS-11 'Sego' is a two-stage lightweight ICBM whose details include a length 65ft 7.5in (20.00m), weights of between 99,205 and 105,820lb (45,000 and 48,000kg) depending on variant with a 2,205lb (1,000kg) payload vehicle in the Models 1 and 2 or a 2,502lb (1,135kg) payload vehicle in the Model 3, propulsion by single storable liquid-propellant rockets in each stage, range of 6,214 miles (10,000km) for the Model 1, 8,080 miles (13,000km) for the Model 2 and 6,585 miles (10,600km) for the Model 3, CEP of 1,530yds (1,400m) for the Model 1 and 1,215yds (1,110m) for the Models 2 and 3, warhead of one 950-kiloton thermonuclear RV in the Model 1, one 950-kiloton thermonuclear RV with penetration aids in the Model 2 and three 100/250-kiloton thermonuclear multiple re-entry vehicles (MRVs) in the Model 3, inertial guidance, and hot launch from a hardened silo with limited reload capability. The SS-11 is a highly capable weapon introduced in 1966, and is a third-generation light ICBM built in very substantial numbers. The Model 1 was distinguished by its single RV and medium range, while the Model 2 of the late 1960s had a single RV and advanced penetration aids, and the Model 3 was an improved operational variant deployed from 1973 with longer range and three MRVs. The Model 4 was a development model of the late 1970s with three or six low-yield Mirvs.

The SS-13 'Savage' is a three-stage lightweight ICBM whose details include a length of 65ft 7.5in (20.00m), weight of 74,955lb (34,000kg) with a 1,499lb (680kg) payload vehicle, three-stage propulsion by liquid-propellant rockets, range of 4,970 miles (8,000km), CEP of 2,025yds (1,850m), warhead of one 600-kiloton nuclear RV, inertial guidance, and hot launch from a silo. Deployed from 1969, the SS-13 is a third-generation light ICBM comparable to the US Minuteman but built and deployed only in small numbers. Other estimates of the type suggest a 750-kiloton warhead carried in a 992lb (450kg) payload vehicle over a range of 6,214 miles (10,000km).

The SS-17 'Spanker' is a two-stage lightweight ICBM whose details include a length of 78ft 9in (24.00m), weight of 143,298lb (65,000kg) with a 6,041lb (2,740kg) post-boost vehicle in the Models 1 and 3 or a 6,019lb (2,730kg) vehicle in the Model 2, two-stage propulsion by storable liquid-propellant rockets, range of 6,214 miles (10,000km) in the Models 1 and 3 or 6,835 miles (11,000km) in the Model 2, CEP of 480yds (440m) in the Model 1, 465yds (425m) in the Model 2 or 385yds (350m) in the Model 3, warhead of four 750-kiloton nuclear Mirvs in the Models 1 and 3 or one 6-megaton thermonuclear RV in the Model 2, inertial guidance, and cold launch from a hardened silo offering a reload capability. The SS-17 is a fourth-generation lightweight ICBM that was introduced in 1975. In its Model 1 form, the type is comparable in performance to the SS-11, but offers the decided strategic advantage of cold launch and thus the opportunity for rapid reload of the silo. The Model 2 was introduced in 1977, and differs from the Model 1 in having a single medium-yield RV and slightly longer range. The Model 3 was introduced in the early 1980s and differs from the Model 1 in having an improved guidance system for reduced CEP: the accuracy of the type enhanced the SS-17 family's capability against US missile silos and thus made it a powerful aspect of the counterforce balance between the USA and the USSR.

The SS-18 'Satan' is a two-stage heavyweight ICBM whose details include a length of 114ft 10in (35.00m), weight of 496,032lb (225,000kg) including the post-boost vehicle that weighs 16,667lb (7,560kg) for the Model 1, 16,733lb (7,590kg) for the Models 2 and 4, and 16,534lb (7,500kg) for the Model 3, two-stage propulsion by storable liquid-propellant rockets, range of 7,455 miles (12,000km) for the Model 1, 6,835 miles (11,000km) for the Models 2 and 4, and 9,940 miles (16,000km) for the Model 3, CEP of 465yds (425m) for the Models 1 and 2, 385yds (350m) for the Model 3 and less than 285yds (260m) for the Model 5, warhead of one 27-megaton thermonuclear RV for the Model 1, eight to ten 900-kiloton thermonuclear Mirvs for the Model 2, one 20-megaton thermonuclear RV for the Model 3, ten 500-kiloton thermonuclear Mirvs for the Model 4, and ten 1-megaton thermonuclear Mirvs for the Model 5, inertial guidance, and cold launch from a hardened silo offering a reload capability. The SS-18 was introduced in 1974 in its Model 1 form, and is a fourth-generation heavyweight ICBM. The weapon is the largest missile so far deployed, and is a truly prodigious weapon with range, accuracy and warhead making it primarily effective as a counterforce weapon against missile silos and buried command/communications centres. The Model 2 followed in 1976, this variant having a computer-controlled post-boost bus with eight or 10 Mirvs. The Model 3 was introduced in 1977, and offers greater range and accuracy than the Model 1 with a slightly smaller but still enormously formidable warhead. The Model 4 was introduced in 1979, and is a derivative of the Model 2 with greater accuracy and an improved post-boost bus carrying up to 14 Mirvs (usually 10 real weapons and four decoys, plus penetration aids). The Model 5 was introduced in the mid-1980s and is still relatively unknown, but is believed to have a range of 5,592 miles (9,000km) with a post-boost bus carrying ten 750-kiloton or 1-megaton thermonuclear Mirvs.

The SS-19 'Stiletto' is a two-stage lightweight ICBM whose details include a length of 73ft 9.5in (22.50m), weight of 171,958lb (78,000kg) with a post-boost vehicle weighing 7,540lb (3,420kg) for the Model 1, 7,011lb (3,180kg) for the Model 2 and 7,518lb (3,410kg) for the Model 3, two-stage propulsion by storable liquid-propellant rockets, range of 5,965 miles (9,600km) for the Model 1 or 6,215 miles (10,000km) for the Models 2 and 3, CEP of 425yds (390m) for the Model 1, 285yds (260m) for the Model 2 and 305yds (280m) for the Model 3, warhead of six 550-kiloton nuclear Mirvs in the Models 1 and 3 or one 10-megaton thermonuclear RV in the Model 2, inertial guidance, and hot launch from a hardened silo with limited reload capability. The SS-19 was introduced in 1975 in its Model 1 form as a lightweight ICBM successor (together with the SS-17) for the SS-11. The type features the same type of advanced guidance as the SS-17 and SS-18, the onboard computer being used either to correct the course (by removing any deviations from the planned norm), or to generate a new course if this is more efficient. Like the SS-17 and SS-18, the SS-19 incorporated the range, accuracy and warhead which made it primarily a counterforce weapon against US missile silos and buried command/communications centres. Introduced in 1978, the Model 2 has a single medium-yield RV and much improved accuracy while the Model 3, introduced in 1980, reverts to a

Currently the most advanced SLBM in the world, the Lockheed UGM-133 Trident II is notable for its long range, very considerable accuracy, and ability to carry a sizeable load of warheads and penetration aids. The type is carried only by the later units of the US Navy's 'Ohio' class submarines and also by the four units of the Royal Navy's 'Vanguard' class.

Mirved payload, but with better accuracy and range than the Model 1. It is believed that surviving Model 1 and 2 weapons were retrofitted to this standard, which could have operational- as well as strategic-level taskings.

The SS-20 'Saber' was a land-mobile IRBM whose details included a length of 54ft 1in (16.49m), weight of 79,365lb (36,000kg), two-stage propulsion by solid-propellant rockets, range of 2,485 miles (4,000km) for the Models 1 and 2 or 4,600 miles (7,400km) for the Model 3, CEP of 465yds (425m), warhead of one 650-kiloton nuclear or 1.5-megaton thermonuclear RV for the Model 1, three 150-kiloton nuclear Mirvs for the Model 2 or one 50-kiloton nuclear RV for the Model 3, inertial guidance, and cold launch from a wheeled transporter/erector/launcher (TEL) with reload capability. The SS-20 was based on the upper two stages of the SS-16 lightweight ICBM and was designed to replace the SS-4 and SS-5 missile systems in the intermediate role. The SS-20 began to enter service in its Model 1 form during 1977 and was a formidable system offering the advantages of good accuracy with tactical land mobility. The warhead was believed to be a 650-kiloton type, although many reports indicate a 1.5-megaton type; this more powerful variant may have entered only limited service. The Model 2 was also introduced in 1977, and offered comparable performance but increased tactical capability through the use of a Mirved warhead. The Model 3 was an increased-range variant with a single low-yield warhead, and may not have entered service.

The SS-24 'Scalpel' is a three-stage ICBM whose details include a length of 69ft 8.5in (21.25m), weight of 220,459lb (100,000kg) with a 7,992lb (3,625kg) post-boost vehicle, three-stage propulsion by solid-propellant rockets, range of 7,455 miles (12,000km) or more, CEP of 202yds (185m), warhead of up to ten 100-kiloton nuclear Mirvs, stellar/inertial guidance, and cold launch from superhardened silos or special railcars offering a reload capability. Entering service in the mid-1980s, the SS-24 was planned as the Soviet fifth-generation counterpart to the US Peacekeeper, and has also been developed for a mobile basing system using special railcars hidden in the tunnels of those parts of the rail network without overhead wires. The type probably entered development in 1974, and suffered a comparatively high number of failures in test launches that began in 1982; the type has been operational since 1985 in its silo-based form and since 1987 in its rail-based form, mainly in northern Russia around Arhangelsk, so it must be assumed that the failings have been overcome in the production weapon, which offers a formidable combination of range, accuracy and warhead. The West believes this missile to be so accurate, that yield estimates for each of the warheads has been reduced from 350 kilotons to 100 kilotons.

Developed as the MX, the Martin LGM-118 Peacekeeper is the USA's most advanced long-range ballistic missile, and as such it is a mighty four-stage weapon designed to deliver up to 10 independently targeted and highly accurate warheads over very long ranges.

The SS-25 'Sickle' is a three-stage lightweight ICBM whose details include a length of 59ft 0.67in (18.00m), weight of 81,570lb (37,000kg) with a post-boost vehicle weight of between 1,499 and 2,205lb (680 and 1,000kg), three-stage propulsion by solid-propellant rockets, a range of 5,590 miles (9,000km) or more, CEP of between 208 and 656yds (190 and 600m), warhead of one 550-kiloton nuclear RV or three/four 150-kiloton nuclear Mirvs, stellar/inertial guidance, and cold launch from a hardened silo or wheeled TEL vehicle offering a reload capability. The SS-25 is intended as an upgraded version of the SS-13 rather than a new design, but the result is a fifth-generation road-mobile weapon with great accuracy, considerably greater throw-weight, and the offensive capability of the US Minuteman lightweight ICBM. The type has largely replaced the SS-11, and is an outgrowth of the SS-13 and SS-16 programmes, the failure of the latter adding impetus to the development of the SS-25 from the early 1970s.

The Martin Marietta LGM-25C Titan II was an American two-stage heavyweight ICBM whose details included a length of 103ft 0in (31.39m), weight of 333,000lb (151,050kg) with a post-boost vehicle weighing 8,300lb (3,765kg) or more, propulsion by two Aerojet LR87-AJ-5 storable liquid-propellant rockets each delivering 216,000lb st (960.81kN) for the first stage and one Aerojet LR91-AH-5 storable liquid-propellant rocket delivering 100,000lb st (444.82kN) for the second stage, range of 9,325 miles (15,000km), CEP of 1,425yds (1,305m), payload of one 9-megaton W53 thermonuclear warhead and penetration aids carried in a single General Electric Mk 6 RV, AC/IBM inertial guidance, and hot launch from a hardened silo. The LGM-25C Titan II was the last of the USA's heavyweight liquid-propellant ICBMs to remain in service, which finished in October 1987 after the type had been introduced in 1962 as successor to the HGM-25A Titan I. The guidance systems were extensively upgraded in 1980 and 1981 to provide effective life into the late 1980s, and the W53 warhead used the same core as the B53 free-fall thermonuclear bomb.

The Boeing LGM-30F Minuteman II is a three-stage lightweight ICBM whose details include a length of 59ft 8.5in (18.20m), approximate weight of 70,000lb (31,750kg) with the TU-120 motor or 72,810lb (33,025kg) with the TU-122 motor and including a post-boost vehicle weighing 1,610lb (730kg), propulsion by one Thiokol M55 (TU-120) or M55A1 (TU-122) solid-propellant rocket delivering 200,600 or 202,600lb st (892.31 or 901.21kN) respectively, one Aerojet SR18-AJ-1 solid-propellant rocket delivering 60,000lb st (266.89kN) for the second stage and one Hercules M57A1 solid-propellant rocket delivering 35,000lb st (155.69kN) for the third stage, range of 7,775 miles (12,510km), CEP of 400yds (365m), payload of one 1.2-megaton W56 thermonuclear warhead carried in an Avco Mk 11C Model 4 RV with Tracor Mk 1A penetration aids, Rockwell Autonetics inertial guidance, and hot launch from a hardened silo. The LGM-30F Minuteman II is a second-generation lightweight ICBM that entered service in 1966, swiftly replacing the LGM-30A and LGM-30B variants of the original

Representing the older generation of American ICBMs, the Convair Atlas was the Western world's first ICBM and its design and development was completed in the period between 1955 and 1960, when this liquid-fuelled weapon reached initial operational capability with a single re-entry vehicle carrying a thermonuclear warhead.

Minuteman I type. The Minuteman II is a simple upgrading of the LGM-30B with more advanced guidance (including an eight-target selection capability and chaff-dispensing penetration aids) and greater range.

The Boeing LGM-30G Minuteman III is a three-stage lightweight ICBM whose details include a length of 59ft 8.5in (18.20m), weight of 78,000lb (35,380kg) including the 2,400lb (1,088kg) Mk 12 or 2,535lb (1,150kg) Mk 12A post-boost vehicles, propulsion by one Thiokol M55A1 (TU-122) solid-propellant rocket delivering 202,600lb st (901.21kN) for the first stage, one Aerojet SR18-AJ-1 solid-propellant rocket delivering 60,625lb st (269.67kN) for the second stage, one Aerojet/Thiokol SR73-AJ/AG-1 solid-propellant rocket delivering 33,800lb st (150.34kN) for the third stage and one Bell Aerospace bi-propellant rocket delivering 315lb st (1.40kN) for the post-boost vehicle, range of 8,700 miles (14,000km), CEP of 300yds (275m) with the Mk 12 RV or 240yds (220m) with the Mk 12A RV, payload of three 170-kiloton W62 nuclear warheads in three General Electric Mk 12 RVs, or three 335-kiloton W78 nuclear warheads in three Mk 12A Mirvs, both types with penetration aids, Rockwell Autonetics inertial guidance, and hot launch from a hardened silo. The LGM-30G Minuteman III Model 1 lightweight ICBM was introduced in 1970 as the third-generation companion to the second-generation Minuteman II, with an improved third stage and Mirved payload, whose Mk 12 bus contains both chaff- and decoy-dispensing penetration aids. The LGM-30G Minuteman III Model 2 was introduced in 1979 as an upgraded model with the improved Mk 12A RV with higher-yield warheads and more advanced penetration aids, made possible by miniaturisation of the warheads and RV components.

The Martin Marietta LGM-118A Peacekeeper is a four-stage heavyweight ICBM whose details include a length of 70ft 10.5in (21.60m), weight of 195,000lb (88,452kg) including the 7,935lb (3,600kg) post-boost vehicle, propulsion by one Thiokol solid-propellant rocket delivering 570,000lb st (2,535.48kN) for the first stage, one Aerojet solid-propellant rocket delivering 335,000lb st (1,490.15kN) for the second stage, one Hercules solid-propellant rocket delivering 77,000lb st (342.51kN) for the third stage and one Rockwell hypergolic liquid-propellant rocket for the fourth stage, range of 8,700 miles (14,000km), CEP of between 65 and 100yds (60 and 90m), payload of ten 335-kiloton W78 thermonuclear warheads carried in 10 Avco Mk 21 (Mk 12 Modified) Mirvs in a Rockwell RS-34 bus, Rockwell Autonetics/Honeywell/Northrop inertial guidance, and cold launch from a hardened silo offering a reload capability. The LGM-118A Peacekeeper was conceived as a replacement for the LGM-25 and LGM-30 series, and as such the Peacekeeper is a fourth-generation heavyweight ICBM. The type was greatly troubled by political opposition during its relatively smooth development life, but the missile, previously known as the Advanced ICBM or MX, entered service during 1986 in upgraded Minuteman silos because political pressure prevented any of the proposed mobile basing methods. The type's accuracy makes it a potent counterforce weapon.

Although China has a small number of submarine-launched ballistic missiles (SLBMs), these are wholly indifferent weapons used mainly for development purposes. The Aérospatiale MSBS M-4 is a French three-stage SLBM whose details include a length of 36ft 3in (11.05m), weight of 77,323lb (35,073kg), propulsion by one SEP 401 (P10) solid-propellant rocket delivering 156,526lb st (696.26kN) for the first stage, one SEP 402 (P6) solid-propellant rocket delivering 66,138lb st (294.20kN) for the second stage and one SEP 403 solid-propellant rocket delivering 15,432lb st (68.45kN) for the third stage, range of 2,796 miles (4,500km) with TN-70 warheads and 3,105 miles (5,000km) or more with TN-71 warheads, CEP of 503yds (460m), warhead of six 150-kiloton TN-70 or miniaturised TN-71 thermonuclear Mirvs, Sagem/EMD inertial guidance, and launch from a submarine tube. Becoming operational in 1985, the M-4 is of a wholly new French SLBM generation designed with considerably greater weight and dimensions for significantly deeper underwater launch depth and improved range with a Mirv bus hardened against electromagnetic pulse and carrying penetration aids. Range is improved with the miniaturised TN-71 warheads, and each system is designed to cover a target area of 217.5 miles (350km) by 93.2 miles (150km). Entering service in the mid-1990s on the new SSBN *Le Triomphant*, the M-4C is an advanced development of the M-4 with longer range, anti-ABM missile features and, probably, the new TN-75 warhead.

The Aérospatiale MSBS M-20 is a two-stage SLBM whose details include a length of 34ft 1.5in (10.40m), weight of 44,213lb (20,055kg), propulsion by one SEP 904 (P10) solid-propellant rocket delivering 99,206lb st (441.29kN) for 50 seconds in the first stage and one SEP Rita 11 (P6) solid-propellant rocket delivering 70,547lb st (313.81kN) for 52 seconds in the second stage, range of 1,864 miles (3,000km), CEP of 1,017yds (930m), warhead of one 1.2-megaton TN-60 thermonuclear device in an MR-60 RV, Sagem/EMD Sagittaire inertial guidance, and launch from a submarine tube. The MSBS M-20 medium-weight SLBM entered service in 1977 as successor to the first-generation M-2, which itself entered service in 1974 as an updated version of the M-1 that was introduced in 1971. The warhead is carried in a modified Rita 11/P6 second stage and is supported by penetration aids. The TN-60 warhead is hardened against the effects of high-altitude nuclear explosions.

The SS-12 'Scaleboard' is a strategic- and operational-level ballistic missile carried on an 8x8 MAZ-543P wheeled transporter/erector/launcher (TEL) and able to deliver its 800-kiloton nuclear warhead over a range of 497 miles (800km) with a CEP of only 33yds (30m).

Two Soviet (now Russian) different approaches to the provision of air defence to ground formations is provided by the ZRK Krug two-missile and ZRK Kub three-missile launchers. The Krug system uses the SA-4 'Ganef' area-defence missile with a sustainer ramjet taking over from four drop-away solid-propellant booster rockets for the delivery of a powerful blast/fragmentation warhead over a range of 31 miles (50km) against any target except one at very low altitude, while the Kub system uses the SA-6 'Gainful' area-defence missile with integrated rocket/ramjet propulsion for the delivery of a smaller blast/fragmentation warhead over a range of 37 miles (60km) against any low- and medium-altitude target. Both missiles have high supersonic performance, and use a mix of command guidance for the mid-course phase on any flight with semi-active radar guidance for the attack phase.

The Soviet SS-N-5 'Sark' is a two-stage SLBM whose details include a 42ft 3.75in (12.90m), weight of 37,477lb (17,000kg), two-stage propulsion by solid-propellant rockets, range of 870 miles (1,400km), CEP of 3,060yds (2,800m), warhead of one 1-megaton thermonuclear RV, inertial guidance, and launch from a submarine tube. Serving in the theatre nuclear role up to the late 1980s on board 13 'Golf II' class missile submarines, the SS-N-5 missile is comparable in many respects to the original version of the US Polaris SLBM, and began to enter service in 1964 as the Soviets' first SLBM with a genuine capability for underwater launch. It is not known with certainty if the type uses solid-propellant or storable liquid-propellant rockets for a range that some sources put as high as 1,490 miles (2,400km).

The SS-N-6 'Serb' is a two-stage SLBM whose details include a length of 32ft 9.75in (10.00m), weight of 41,667lb (18,900kg) including a 1,499lb (680kg) post-boost vehicle, two-stage propulsion by storable liquid-propellant rockets, range of 1,490 miles (2,400km) for the Model 1 and 1,865 miles (3,000km) for the Models 2 and 3, CEP of 2,025yds (1,850m), warhead of one 700-kiloton nuclear RV for the Model 1, or one 650-kiloton nuclear RV for the Model 2 or two 350-kiloton nuclear MRVs for the Model 3, inertial guidance, and launch from a submarine tube. The SS-N-6 Model 1 was introduced in 1970 as a hybrid second/third-generation SLBM using technology and components derived from the SS-11. The warhead size and comparatively poor CEP dictate the weapon's targeting against area targets. Introduced in 1973, the Model 2 trades throw-weight for range, the reduction of 50 kilotons in warhead yield providing an additional 373 miles (600km) of range to provide launch submarines with a larger operating area. The Model 3 was introduced in 1974 and combines the range of the Model 2 with a double warhead configuration for maximum effect against cities and other area targets.

The SS-N-8 'Sawfly' is a two-stage SLBM whose details include a length of 42ft 3.75in (12.90m), weight of 44,974lb (20,400kg) including a 1,499lb (680kg) post-boost vehicle, two-stage propulsion by storable liquid-propellant rockets, range of 4,845 miles (7,800km) for the Model 1 and 5,655 miles (9,100km) for the Model 2, CEP of 1,540yds (1,410m) for the Model 1 and 1,695yds (1,550m) for the Model 2, warhead of one 1.2-megaton nuclear RV for the Model 1 and one or two 800-kiloton nuclear MRVs for the Model 2, stellar/inertial guidance, and launch from a submarine tube. Introduced in 1971 on board 'Delta I' class SSBNs, the SS-N-8 Model 1 is a fourth-generation SLBM with good range but only moderate CEP despite the use of two stellar fixes to update the inertial guidance. Introduced in 1977, the Model 2 is a developed version carrying the same weight of warhead over greater range.

The SS-N-17 'Snipe' is a two-stage SLBM whose details include a length of 36ft 3.5in (11.06m), an unrevealed weight including a 2,502lb (1,135kg) post-boost vehicle, two-stage propulsion by solid-propellant rockets, range of 2,425 miles (3,900km), CEP of 1,530yds (1,400m), warhead of one 500-kiloton or 1-megaton thermonuclear RV, stellar/inertial guidance, and launch from a submarine tube. Introduced in 1977 on the sole 'Yankee II' class SSBN, the SS-N-17 was the first Soviet SLBM known to have solid-propellant rockets. It is also believed that the type has post-boost propulsion for manoeuvring in space, yet the CEP is still too great for the missile's use in anything but the countervalue role.

The SS-N-18 'Stingray' is a two-stage SLBM whose details include a length of 46ft 3.25in (14.10m), weight of 55,115lb (25,000kg), two-stage propulsion by storable liquid-propellant rockets, range of 4,040 miles (6,500km) for the Models 1 and 3 or 4,970 miles (8,000km) for the Model 2, CEP of 1,540yds (1,410m) for the Models 1 and 3 or 1,695yds (1,550m) for the Model 2, warhead of three 200-kiloton nuclear Mirvs for the Model 1, one 450-kiloton nuclear RV for the Model 2 and seven 200-kiloton nuclear Mirvs for the Model 3, stellar/inertial guidance, and launch from a submarine tube. The SS-N-18 Model 1 is a fourth-generation SLBM that entered service in 1976 aboard 'Delta III' class SSBNs, and was the first Soviet SLBM with a Mirved warhead. The Model 2 was introduced in 1979 and offers greater range with a payload

The AT-1 'Snapper' was the Soviets' first-generation anti-tank missile, and was a relatively simple weapon with command-to-line-of-sight guidance using commands passed to the missile via a trailing wire link.

reduced to one RV. The Model 3 was also introduced in 1979 as successor to the Model 1 with a load of seven smaller Mirvs.

The SS-N-20 'Sturgeon' is a three-stage SLBM with a length of 49ft 2.5in (15.00m), unrevealed weight, three-stage propulsion by solid-propellant rockets, range of 5,160 miles (8,300km), CEP of 547yds (500m), warhead of between six and nine 100/200-kiloton Mirvs, stellar/inertial guidance, and launch from a submarine tube. Introduced in 1981 as the primary armament of the huge 'Typhoon' class SSBN, the SS-N-20 entered development in 1973 as a fifth-generation SLBM of good range and advanced capabilities.

The SS-N-23 'Skiff' is a two-stage SLBM whose details include a length of 44ft 7.5in (13.60m), unrevealed weight, two-stage propulsion by storable liquid-propellant rockets, range of 5,160 miles (8,300km), CEP of 612yds (560m), warhead of seven 150-kiloton nuclear Mirvs, stellar/inertial guidance, and launch from a submarine tube. Introduced in 1985 aboard the 'Delta IV' class SSBN, the SS-N-23 is a capable fifth-generation SLBM notable for its good range and low CEP. Some estimates put the number of Mirvs as high as 10, and it is possible that the type will be retrofitted in the 'Delta III' class SSBNs as replacement for the shorter-ranged SS-N-18 series.

Now used only by the UK in its UGM-27C Polaris A3TK Chevaline form, the Lockheed UGM-27A Polaris was designed in the USA as the world's first SLBM. The details of this considerably updated British two-stage SLBM include a length of 32ft 3.5in (9.84m), weight of 35,000lb (15,876kg) including a 1,500lb (680kg) post-boost vehicle, propulsion by one Aerojet A3P solid-propellant rocket delivering 80,000lb st (355.86kN) for the first stage and one Hercules solid-propellant rocket for the second stage, range of 2,950 miles (4,750km), CEP of 1,015yds (930m), payload of three 200-kiloton W58 nuclear warheads carried in three MRVs plus an unknown number of decoys and penetration aids on the basic Penetration Air Carrier (post-boost bus), General Electric/MIT/Hughes/Raytheon Mk 2 inertial guidance, and launch from a submarine tube. As noted above, this is now the only version of the Polaris SLBM left in service, the missiles having been updated in the 'Chevaline' programme of the 1970s to carry (and instead of the original three British 200-kiloton warheads) several British MRVs capable of a 45 mile (72km) lateral separation. The warheads are hardened against electromagnetic pulse and fast radiation, and the warhead bus also contains chaff penetration aids and several decoys.

The Lockheed UGM-73A Poseidon C3 is a two-stage SLBM whose details include a length of 34ft 0in (10.36m), weight of 65,000lb (29,484kg) including the 3,300lb (1,497kg) post-boost vehicle, propulsion by two Thiokol/Hercules solid-propellant rockets for the first stage and two Hercules solid-propellant rockets for the second stage, range of 2,485 miles (4,000km) with 14 Mirvs or 3,230 miles (5,200km) with 10 Mirvs, CEP of 605yds (553m), payload of ten 40/50-kiloton W68 nuclear warheads carried in 10 Mk 3 Mirvs, or 14 W76 100-kiloton nuclear warheads carried in 14 Mk 3 Mirvs, General Electric/MIT/Hughes/Raytheon Mk 4 inertial guidance, and launch from a submarine tube. Introduced in 1970 as successor to the Polaris SLBM, the Poseidon marked an eightfold increase in target-devastation capability at the same range as its predecessor, the Poseidon's real advantages being much improved CEP and a Mirved payload.

The Lockheed UGM-96A Trident I C4 is a three-stage SLBM whose details include a length of 34ft 0in (10.36m), weight of 73,000lb (33,113kg) including a powered post-boost vehicle weighing more than 3,000lb (1,361kg), propulsion by one Thiokol/Hercules solid-propellant rocket for the first stage, one Hercules solid-propellant rocket for the second stage and one UTC-CSD solid-propellant rocket for the third stage, range of 4,230

The Aérospatiale Pluton was designed for French army use in the battlefield nuclear role, and is a small inertially guided surface-to-surface weapon carried in its container/launcher on an adapted AMX-30 main battle tank chassis for the delivery of a 15-kiloton nuclear warhead.

miles (6,810km), CEP of 500yds (457m), payload of eight 100-kiloton W76 nuclear warheads carried in eight Mk 4 Mirvs, Mk 5 stellar/inertial guidance, and launch from a submarine tube. The UGM-96A Trident I C4 was introduced in 1979 as the primary armament of the 'Ohio' class SSBNs and was also carried in a number of converted 'Benjamin Franklin' and 'Lafayette' class SSBNs. The Trident I is essentially the Poseidon SLBM with a third stage for greatly increased range and a more advanced warhead based on the Mk 4 Mirv, the bus being manoeuvrable in space for maximum accuracy. The Lockheed UGM-133A Trident II D5 entered service in the late 1980s as a much improved development for use in the 'Ohio' class SSBN. The type has a length of 44ft 6.6in (13.58m), launch weight of 130,000lb (58,968kg) and a range of 7,500 miles (12,070km). The first two stages have graphite-epoxy rather than Kevlar casings but contain the same basic motors as the Trident I with a burn time of about 65 seconds each, while the third stage has a United Technologies motor with a burn time of about 40 seconds for a burn-out speed of about 13,635mph (21,943km/h). The payload comprises 10 to 15 Mk 5 RVs each with one 335-kiloton W78 warhead, and guidance is entrusted to the Mk 6 stellar-inertial system offering a CEP as low as 130yds (120m). The Royal Navy's version will probably have eight British-designed warheads in a US-provided manoeuvring bus.

Surface-to-surface missiles also include shorter-range weapons intended for the operational- and tactical-level roles. The CPMIEC Model M is typical of the Chinese concept in such weapons, and is a single-stage surface-to-surface theatre/battlefield missile with a length of 29ft 10.25in (9.10m), weight of 13,668lb (6,200kg), propulsion by one solid-propellant rocket, range of up to 373 miles (600km), an HE/fragmentation warhead, inertial guidance, and launch from a wheeled TEL vehicle. This weapon has been developed with HE/fragmentation and submunition-dispenser warheads, although a tactical nuclear warhead is also a possibility. Flight trials apparently began in 1986, with service deliveries beginning in late 1988 or early 1989. Ranges between 124 and 373 miles (200 and 600km) are possible, and the export version is designated M-9.

The Aérospatiale Pluton is a French single-stage surface-to-surface battlefield missile with a length of 25ft 0.75in (7.64m), weight of 5,342lb (2,423kg), propulsion by one SEP/SNPE/Aérospatiale dual-thrust solid-propellant rocket, range limits of 6.2 and 75 miles (10 and 120km), CEP of 360yds (330m), a 772lb (350kg) 15-kiloton nuclear or 1,102lb (500kg) 25-kiloton AN-51 nuclear warhead, SFENA strapdown inertial guidance, and launch from a box on a converted AMX-30 MBT chassis. Designed in the late 1960s, the Pluton entered French service in 1974 and is a capable battlefield weapon with fair accuracy for use primarily against operational-level targets such as transport centres and follow-on troop concentrations; the larger warhead contains the same MR50 nuclear charge as used in the CEA-developed AN-52 free-fall store carried by French strike aircraft.

The Defence Research and Development Laboratory Prithvi is an Indian single-stage surface-to-surface battlefield missile of which few details are known. The type is powered by one solid-propellant rocket, has a maximum range of 155 miles (250km) and possesses strapdown inertial guidance. First revealed late in 1988, this is a weapon of odd appearance with a comparatively short and fat body, a cruciform of low-aspect-ratio wings half-way down the body, and a cruciform of tiny rectangular fins (indexed in line with the wings) at the tail. The type can be fitted with any of several types of conventional warhead, and there are suggestions that a nuclear warhead could be retrofitted.

The Ching Feng is a Taiwanese single-stage surface-to-surface battlefield missile with a length of 22ft 11.5in (7.00m), weight of 3,086lb (1,400kg), propulsion by one solid-propellant rocket, maximum range of 75 miles (120km), HE warhead and radar-based guidance system. This 'Green Bee' missile appears to be based conceptually on the US Lance, although the fins are somewhat smaller and a radar guidance system is used. The weapon was revealed in 1981 and has since been claimed to be the precursor of a more formidable missile with a 621 mile (1,000km) range, which may explain the apparent cancellation of the programme under pressure from the USA, which feared the strategic and political implications of Taiwanese possession of a potentially nuclear-capable missile system able to reach targets on the Chinese mainland.

The FROG-3 is a Soviet (now Russian) two-stage surface-to-surface battlefield unguided rocket rather than guided missile with a length of 34ft 5.5in (10.50m), weight of 4,960lb (2,250kg), propulsion by one non-jettisonable solid-propellant booster rocket and one solid-propellant sustainer rocket, maximum range of 25 miles (40km), CEP of 435yds (400m), warhead of one interchangeable 200-kiloton nuclear or 992lb (450kg) HE type, warheads, and launch from a converted PT-76 amphibious light tank chassis. Oldest of the Free Rocket Over Ground (FROG) series still in service, the FROG-3 was introduced in 1957 and now possesses little real value as its CEP is so great. The FROG-5 is an improved two-stage surface-to-surface battlefield rocket with a length of 29ft 10.25in (9.10m), weight of 6,614lb (3,000kg), propulsion by one non-jettisonable solid-propellant booster rocket and one solid-propellant sustainer rocket, maximum range of 34 miles (55km), CEP of 435yds (400m), warhead of one interchangeable 200-kiloton nuclear and 992lb (450kg) HE type, and launch from a converted PT-76 amphibious light tank chassis. Introduced in the late 1950s or early 1960s, this is a development of the FROG-3 with a revised

Carried on a variant of the PT-76 light amphibious tank's chassis, the FROG-3 was a Soviet artillery rocket without guidance, and could deliver a 200-kiloton nuclear or alternative conventional warhead over a range of 25 miles (40km) with only limited accuracy.

propulsion system, the body of the rocket being increased in diameter to that of the FROG-3's warhead, in the process being slightly shortened. Like the FROG-3, the FROG-5 is now of little operational value. The FROG-7 is a single-stage surface-to-surface battlefield rocket with a length of 29ft 10.25in (9.10m), weight of 5,071lb (2,300kg), propulsion by one solid-propellant rocket, range limits of 6.8 and 43 miles (11 and 70km), CEP of between 490 and 765yds (450 and 700m) depending on range, warhead of one 1,213lb (550kg) 10-, 100- or 200-kiloton nuclear type, or 1,213lb (550kg) HE or 860lb (390kg) chemical type, and launch from a ZIL-135 8x8 TEL vehicle. The FROG-7A was introduced in 1965 as the last of the FROG series weapons, and is being replaced by the longer-ranged and more accurate SS-21. The FROG-7B is an improved version that is also in service with Iraq, which has developed an improved Laith model able to carry a cluster-munition warhead over a range of 55.9 miles (90km).

The SS-1C 'Scud-B' is a Soviet (now Russian) single-stage surface-to-surface battlefield missile with a length of 37ft 4.75in (11.40m), weight of 14,043lb (6,370kg), propulsion by one storable liquid-propellant rocket, range limits of 50 and 112 miles (80 and 180km) with a nuclear warhead, or 50 and 174 miles (80 and 280km) with an HE or chemical warhead, CEP of 1,015yds (930m) at maximum range and reducing with shorter range, a warhead of one 40/100-kiloton variable-yield nuclear or 4,409lb (2,000kg) HE or chemical type, inertial guidance, and launch from a MAZ-543 8x8 TEL vehicle. The SS-1A 'Scunner' was introduced in 1957 as the original operational model of this series, but is no longer in front-line service with Warsaw Pact countries. It was a considerably less capable weapon than its successors, having a weight of 9,700lb (4,400kg) and able to carry a 40-kiloton (later an HE) warhead over a range of 81 miles (130km) after launch from its TEL, a converted IS-III heavy tank chassis. The SS-1B 'Scud-A' was introduced in 1965 as an altogether more capable weapon. The SS-1C 'Scud-B' was introduced in about 1970, and this variant has a maximum range boosted to 280 miles (450km) by a better propellant load, but maximum-range CEP increases to 1,205yds (1,100m) as a consequence. With an HE rather than nuclear warhead the missile has been exported to a number of

Carried on the ZIL-135 8x8 wheeled chassis, the FROG-7 was introduced to Soviet service in 1965, and was the last of the Free Rocket Over Ground series of unguided battlefield rockets, and in this instance could carry any of three nuclear or two conventional (HE or chemical) warheads over a range of 43 miles (70km) with the indifferent accuracy typical of large rockets in this period.

Moslem countries, and of these Iraq has produced two upgraded variants, namely the Al Hussein and the Al Abas: the Al Hussein has considerably greater range than the 'Scud-B', this figure of 373 miles (600km) being achieved by reducing the warhead's explosive load to 551lb (250kg) and by a lengthening of the missile by some 4ft 3.25in (1.3m) to boost fuel load by 2,293lb (1,040kg) to just over 11,023lb (5,000kg); in the Al Abas the weight of explosive in the warhead is further reduced to 419lb (190kg), allowing a further increment in range to 534 miles (860km). These Iraqi variants have greater CEPs than the baseline Soviet missile, and have been used with chemical rather than HE warheads.

The SS-12B 'Scaleboard-B' is another Soviet (now Russian) single-stage short-range ballistic missile with a length of 40ft 7.5in (12.38m), weight of 19,841lb (9,000kg), propulsion by four solid-propellant rockets, range limits of 138 and 497 miles (220 and 800km), CEP of 33yds (30m), warhead of one 2,756lb (1,250kg) 800-kiloton nuclear type, inertial guidance with infra-red terminal homing for the very low CEP, and launch from a MAZ-543P 8x8 TEL vehicle. The SS-12A 'Scaleboard-A' was introduced in 1969 to provide the Soviet army with long-range strategic/operational capability at front (army group) level. The SS-12B 'Scaleboard-B' was originally designated SS-22 in Western terminology and subsequently redesignated SS-12M in acknowledgement of the Soviet claim that the missile was a development of the SS-12 rather than a new type. This improved SS-12 entered service in 1979, and has different ranges (138 to 547 miles; 220 to 880km) combined with reduced CEP (the original figure of 350yds/320m having been considerably reduced in recent years) and alternative 550-kiloton or 1-megaton nuclear warheads that can each be exchanged for a chemical or cluster-munition warhead.

The SS-21 'Scarab' is a Soviet (now Russian) single-stage surface-to-surface battlefield missile with a length of 30ft 10.25in (9.44m), weight of 6,614lb (3,000kg), propulsion by one solid-propellant rocket, range limits of 8.75 to 125 miles (14 to 200km), CEP of between 55 and 100yds (50 and 100m), warhead of one 10- or 100-kiloton nuclear, or 992lb (450kg) HE (unitary, anti-armour cluster, anti-personnel cluster or anti-runway) or chemical type, inertial guidance, and launch from a ZIL-5937 6x6 TEL vehicle. The SS-21 was introduced in 1976 as replacement for the FROG series, and was deployed at front (army group) level as a primary means of removing NATO defensive positions that might slow or halt the main axes of Soviet advance.

The SS-23 'Spider' is a Soviet (now Russian) single-stage short-range ballistic missile (SRBM) with a length of 24ft 8in (7.52m), weight of 10,340lb (4,690kg), propulsion by one solid-propellant rocket, range limits of 50 and 311 miles (80 and 500km), CEP of 33yds (30m), warhead of one 992lb (450kg) 100-kiloton nuclear, chemical or cluster-munition type, inertial guidance with active radar terminal homing, and launch from a MAZ-543 8x8 TEL vehicle. Introduced in 1980, this is the Soviet replacement for the 'Scud' series, and offers significantly reduced time into action as well as better range and CEP, the latter having been reduced in Western analysis to the current figure when it became apparent that the missile is a member of the Soviet 'reconnaissance strike' family with terminal guidance.

The SS-1C 'Scud-B' was designed for carriage and launch from the MAZ-543 8x8 TEL vehicle, and for the time of its introduction in about 1970 was a capable battlefield missile with inertial guidance for the fairly accurate delivery of a moderately large nuclear, HE or chemical warhead over a range of 112 miles (180km) with the nuclear warhead or 174 miles (280km) with the lighter HE or chemical warheads.

Introduced in 1976 as replacement for the FROG series of unguided battlefield rockets, the SS-21 'Scarab' is an inertially guided missile carried on the ZIL-5937 6x8 TEL vehicle that is basically similar to that of the ZRK Romb used with the SA-8 'Gecko' surface-to-air missile system. The SS-21 offers considerable accuracy to a maximum range of 125 miles (200km), and this allows effective use of conventional (chemical, unitary HE or cluster HE) warheads as an alternative to the 10- or 100- kiloton nuclear warhead.

The Douglas MGR-1B Honest John was an American single-stage surface-to-surface battlefield rocket rather than a missile, with a length of 24ft 10in (7.57m), weight of 4,710lb (2,136kg), propulsion by one solid-propellant rocket, range limits of 4.5 and 23 miles (7.2 and 37km), CEP of 910yds (830m), warhead of one 2-, 20- or 40-kiloton W31 nuclear, or 1,500lb (680kg) HE or cluster munition, or 1,243lb (564kg) chemical type, and launch from a 6x6 truck TEL vehicle. The MGR-1B was introduced in 1960 to replace the 1953-vintage MGR-1A initial version. The MGR-1B is an obsolescent system combining a powerful warhead and good cross-country mobility with the accuracy and range of tube artillery, but in the non-nuclear role it offers limited offensive capability and at considerable cost.

The Martin Marietta MGM-31B Pershing II is an American two-stage medium-range ballistic missile with a length of 34ft 5.5in (10.50m), weight of 16,000lb (7,257kg), propulsion by one Hercules XM101 solid-propellant rocket for the first stage and one Hercules solid-propellant rocket for the second stage, maximum range of 1,125 miles (1,810km), CEP of between 22 and 49yds (20 and 45m), warhead of one 650lb (295kg) 5/50-kiloton selectable-yield W85 air/surface-burst or W86 earth-penetrating nuclear type, Singer-Kearfott inertial guidance with Goodyear RADAR active radar terminal homing, and launch from an M656 truck/trailer-mounted TEL vehicle. The MGM-31A Pershing IA was introduced in 1969 as a long-range battlefield interdiction missile derived from the 1962-vintage MGM-31 Pershing I deployed on the M474 tracked launch vehicle. The Pershing IA changed to the M656 truck/trailer TEL, was 34ft 9.5in (10.60m) long, weighed 10,140lb (4,600kg), was powered by one Thiokol XM105 solid-propellant booster rocket delivering 26,750lb st (118.99kN) and one Thiokol XM106 solid-propellant sustainer rocket delivering 15,560lb st (69.21kN), and carried a 1,650lb (748kg) 60/400-kiloton variable-yield W50 air-burst nuclear warhead over a range of between 100 and 460 miles (161 and 740km) with a CEP of 400yds (365m) under the guidance of a Bendix inertial navigation system. The MGM-31B Pershing II was introduced in 1985 as a modular upgrading of the Pershing IA with far greater range and other system improvements, the most important of which was the radar area guidance (RADAG) terminal homing, which reduced the CEP to so low a figure that a much smaller warhead (W85 surface/air-burst or W86 earth-penetrator) could be carried. The range and extreme accuracy of the weapon meant that even with a small warhead the type had operational and indeed limited strategic capabilities within the European theatre. The type was phased out of service as a result of the Intermediate Nuclear Forces Treaty.

The Vought MGM-52C Lance is an American single-stage battlefield support missile with a length of 20ft 3in (6.17m), weight of 3,373lb (1,530kg) with a nuclear warhead or 3,920lb (1,778kg) with a conventional warhead, propulsion by two Rocketdyne T22 dual-thrust storable liquid-propellant rockets, range limits of 3 and 75 miles (4.8 and 121km), CEP of 500yds (455m), warhead of one 467lb (212kg) 1-, 10- or 50-kiloton selectable-yield W70-1/2/3 nuclear or 0.5-kiloton enhanced-radiation W70-4 nuclear, or 1,000lb (454kg) M251 cluster-munition type, E-Systems/Sys-Donner/Arma simplified inertial guidance, and launch from an M752 tracked TEL vehicle. The MGM-52C was introduced in 1972 as replacement for the Sergeant and Honest John weapons. The Lance is a highly capable but obsolescent battlefield missile able to deliver an assortment of alternative warheads, including the W70-4 'neutron' type and the M251 cluster-munition type with 836 0.95lb (0.43kg) anti-personnel/anti-matériel bomblets to saturate a circle of 900yds (820m) diameter.

Anti-ship missiles fall into two basic types as surface- and air-launched weapons, the latter often being derivatives of the former without the booster rockets used to launch and accelerate the missiles.

The China Precision Machine Import and Export Corporation C-101 is very little known, although it is thought to represent another step in the Chinese evolution of air- and surface-launched anti-ship missiles derived ultimately from the Soviet P-15 (SS-N-2 'Styx') of which the Chinese received numerous examples in the late 1950s. The P-15 was developed into the Hai Ying 1 coast-launched anti-ship missile that received the combined US and NATO reporting designation CSSC-2 'Silkworm', and it is thought that the C-101 is an air-launched derivative of the HY-1 with two small ramjets for sustainer power. On release from a launch warplane, the missile falls some 195ft (60m) before the rocket booster ignites, accelerating the missile to Mach 1.8. At this point the two laterally mounted ramjets are ignited, further accelerating the weapon to Mach 2. The missile cruises at a height of 150ft (50m), and at a range of 3,280yds (3,000m) from the target it descends to sea-skimming height before impacting the target about 16.4ft (5m) above the waterline. Notable features of this weapon, known only by its Chinese export designation, are two outward-canted swept fins above the booster rocket section and two equally sized rectangular vertical surfaces, each with an inset rudder, in the dorsal and ventral position just forward of the booster rocket section.

The CPMIEC Ying Ji-1 (Eagle Strike-1) weapon is an advanced anti-ship missile about which little is known. The weapon was developed from the mid-1970s and was first publicly revealed in 1984 in its original surface-launched form, intended for use by coastal defence forces, warships and surfaced submarines with the aid of a fire-control system basically similar to that used with the Chinese HY-1 and HY-2 derivatives of the Soviet SS-N-2 'Styx'. The missile can also be launched from warplanes. The missile is based on a substantial body of cylindrical section with a tapered nosecone comprising the radome over the active radar seeker used for terminal guidance. This body is carried by a mid-set cruciform of cropped delta wings, and control is provided by a tail-mounted cruciform of smaller moving control fins, also of cropped delta configuration and indexed in line with the wings. Unlike the surface-launched versions of the weapon, which are fired with the aid of a solid-propellant booster rocket section that is discarded on burn-out, the air-launched weapon is merely released from its launch warplane (generally the Nanchang Q-5 'Fantan' attack fighter) and, once it has fallen for a set time, ignites its rocket motor for high-speed cruise at a pre-set altitude of some 82ft (25m) under control of its inertial guidance package, descending to 16.4ft (5m) for the sea-skimming terminal phase of the attack under active radar control. The YJ-1 was probably entering Chinese service only in the mid-1990s, and although the weapon is also offered on the export market, there have been no known sales of this C-801 version. First reported in 1988, the YJ-2 is a longer-range development of the YJ-1 with the body lengthened for the incorporation of a small turbofan engine, aspirated via a ventral inlet, in place of the YJ-1's rocket motor. The revised missile weighs 1,576lb (715kg) and is thought to possess a range of 74.6 miles (120km). The current status of this improved YJ-2 weapon is not clear, but the type has been offered on the export market with the revised designation C-802.

The standard French anti-ship missile is the Aérospatiale Exocet. Second only to the McDonnell Douglas Harpoon as the most widely produced anti-ship missile of Western origins, the Exocet was designed from 1967 originally as the MM.38 ship-launched missile which entered service in 1975. Since that date the missile has been developed in several forms and has seen extensive operational use, notably in the Falklands War (1982) and

The Aérospatiale Exocet is the Western world's second most important anti-ship missile after the McDonnell Douglas Harpoon series, and is a potent weapon with an advanced warhead whose destructive effect is enhanced by the detonation of any residual fuel. The type has been produced in several forms for ship-, air- and submarine-launched use, and illustrated here is the baseline MM.38 ship-launched weapon (bottom) and MM.40 improved ship-launched weapon (inset). In the MM.40 version the use of a lighter container/launcher allows the weapon to be carried on smaller vessels despite the greater weight of the missile, which is fitted with a longer and heavier rocket-motor section for a range of 43.5 (70km) rather than 28 miles (45km).

The AM.39 (inboard) is the standard air-launched version of the Aérospatiale Exocet anti-ship missile, and has been used with considerable success in two wars.

in the Iraqi-Iranian Gulf War (1980-88). Development of the AM.38 as the Exocet's air-launched version began in 1975, and the first round was test-fired in December 1976 to allow service entry in 1977. This initial AM.38 was a limited-production helicopter-launched version of the MM.38 using SNPE Epervier booster and SNPE Eole V sustainer rocket motors with concentric nozzles. A delay of one second was built into the booster rocket's ignition sequence to avoid damage to the launch platform. Entering service in 1979, the AM.39 is the full-production version of the MM.38 optimised for air launch with a revised propulsion arrangement in a shorter body, thus reducing weight but increasing range. The basic configuration of the Exocet is of the 'classic' air-launched anti-ship missile type, with a cylindrical body terminating at its forward end in an ogivally tapered nose that constitutes the radome over the antenna for the active radar, a mid-set cruciform of cropped delta wings, and a tail-mounted cruciform of smaller control fins indexed in line with the wings. The missile is launched toward the target on range and bearing data provided by the launch warplane's sensors and fire-control system, and after the two-second acceleration phase by the Condor booster rocket, the Hélios sustainer rocket fires for 150 seconds as the missile cruises at low altitude until some 6.2 miles (10km) from the target's anticipated position, when the monopulse active seeker head is turned on, the target acquired and the terminal phase initiated at one of three heights preselected at launch (on the basis of anticipated sea state in the target area). Residual fuel adds considerably to the effects of the warhead detonation, which has in itself proved somewhat troublesome and unreliable. Late-production rounds have the Super ADAC frequency-agile homing radar with digital signal processing, which offers the considerable tactical advantage of improved resistance to electronic countermeasures (ECM) as well as the ability to discriminate between real targets and features such as decoys and coastal features. This improvement package also adds an upgraded inertial platform allowing the missile to fly at a height of between 6.6 and 9.8ft (2 and 3m) and also to make pre-programmed manoeuvres.

The MBB Kormoran 1 entered West German naval service as the primary anti-ship weapon of Lockheed F-104G Starfighters operated by the Marineflieger, and is now used on the Panavia Tornado IDS warplanes operated by the same service and by the Italian air force. The origins of the missile can be traced to 1962, when the West German defence ministry contracted with Bölkow K.G. for a study designed to highlight the capabilities and limitations of current air-to-surface missiles, and a similar study was undertaken in France by Nord-Aviation, which was largely responsible for the AS.33 missile that had been designed to a Franco-West German requirement. In 1967, MBB was contracted to produce a production-standard version of the AS.33 as the AS.34 that later received the

German name Kormoran. The new weapon was tested in 1974, and in 1976 MBB received an initial contract for 350 Kormoran anti-ship missiles, in a programme that saw delivery of the last missiles in 1983. The Kormoran is of classic air-launched anti-ship missile and also of typical Nord missile configuration. The weapon is based on a cylindrical body of considerable diameter and terminating at its forward end in the ogival radome over the antenna for the terminal guidance package's active radar. The body carries two sets of flying surfaces in the forms of a mid-set cruciform of swept delta wings with cropped tips, and a smaller cruciform of tail-mounted control fins indexed in line with the wings. After launch from its parent warplane, the missile is accelerated by the 1-second thrust of its two booster rocket motors, and then cruises under the 100-second thrust of its sustainer rocket motor at a height of 100ft (30m) to the approximate location of the target, where it descends to wave-top height for the pre-set active or passive radar attack. The warhead is a particularly impressive feature of the missile, being designed to penetrate up to 3.54in (90mm) of metal before the 16 radially disposed charges detonate to pierce the ship's bottom, decks and internal bulkheads.

The Kormoran 2 is an improved model weighing 1,389lb (630kg) and fitted with a new Thomson-CSF solid-state radar seeker. The weapon has the same airframe as the Kormoran 1, but replacement of the earlier weapon's analogue electronics by more advanced and less bulky digital electronics provides the additional volume for a larger 485lb (220kg) semi-armour-piercing blast/fragmentation warhead of greater penetration capability. The digital electronics also improve hit probability, increase the guidance package's resistance to countermeasures, enhance reliability, and simplify launch procedures. The Kormoran 2 also has an uprated powerplant for higher speed and modestly improved range. Development of the Kormoran 2 started in 1983, and a small series of successful test launches was completed in October 1990. The German navy has a requirement for between 175 and 210 examples of the new missile type, but the collapse of the USSR as an effective threat to western Europe in the late 1980s has meant a postponement if not cancellation of any production order.

The Israel Aircraft Industries Gabriel Mk IIIA/S is the air-launched version of the ship-launched Gabriel Mk III anti-ship missile, itself derived from the earlier Gabriel Mks I and II. The Gabriel Mk I was developed in the 1960s as a surface-launched missile with a range of 13.05 miles (21km) and

The McDonnell Douglas Harpoon is a comparatively small anti-ship missile that can be fired from air, surface and submarine platforms. The type has a powerful warhead and an advanced guidance package that has been considerably improved in successive variants of the missile, and secures a considerable range from the use of a sustainer turbojet for the main part of the flight after the missile has been launched, as in this RGM-84 shipborne model, by a solid-propellant rocket-motor section that is then jettisoned.

optimised for deployment on fast attack craft, while the Gabriel Mk II introduced a longer body for more fuel as a means of boosting range to 22.4 miles (36km). The ship-launched Gabriel Mk III introduced a frequency-agile active radar seeker, although the optical and semi-active radar homing systems of the Gabriel Mks I and II can also be used to provide greater tactical flexibility and continued operability in the face of enemy ECM. The Gabriel Mk III can thus have three guidance modes, namely fire-and-forget, fire-and-update via a data link from a targeting helicopter, and fire-and-command using the launch vessel's radar for better targeting data. The missile cruises at 330ft (100m) and then descends to 66ft (20m) for its approach to the target, the attack phase being flown at a pre-set height of 4.9, 8.25 or 13.1ft (1.5, 2.5 or 4m) depending on the anticipated sea state in the target area. The Gabriel Mk IIIA/S has a slightly longer body, reduced-span wings and lighter weight, which all contribute to higher speed but shorter range. The missile has three operating modes: range-and-bearing launch using radar-derived data, range-and-bearing launch using manually entered data, and bearing-only launch. In its basic layout the Gabriel is of typical anti-ship missile configuration, with a cylindrical body terminating forward in the ogival nosecone that constitutes the radome for the active radar guidance's antenna, a mid-set cruciform of fixed wings, and a tail-mounted cruciform of moving control fins indexed in line with the wings.

The Gabriel Mk IIIA/S ER is an extended-range version with a longer sustainer rocket that increases maximum range to 37.3 miles (60km), which is similar to that of the ship-launched Gabriel Mk III variant. Both the Gabriel Mk IIIA/S and Mk IIIA/S ER have the same guidance options as the basic Gabriel Mk III. The Gabriel Mk IVLR is an updated version developed during the early 1990s for a service debut in the middle of the decade. Although it is clearly related to the Gabriel Mk III, the Gabriel Mk IV is a somewhat larger and more massive weapon with turbojet sustainer propulsion for longer range and with a more potent warhead. The Gabriel Mk IV weighs 2,116lb (960kg) with its 529lb (240kg) proximity- and impact-fused semi-armour-piercing blast/fragmentation warhead, and its

One of the most important missiles used by the Israeli navy, and also by the South African and Taiwanese navies, is the Gabriel anti-ship missile developed by Israel Military Industries. This has been developed and produced for shipborne and air-launched use in several forms, that illustrated here being an example of the Gabriel I baseline shipborne weapon with the option of several guidance modes to enhance its versatility and resistance to enemy countermeasures.

The first anti-ship missile to enter Western service, the Norwegian-designed Kongsberg Penguin is still a capable weapon in its later forms, including this air-launched version that can be programmed to fly a dog-leg approach to the target area under the control of an inertial system before making its attack under control of a passive infra-red system.

propulsion arrangement uses a solid-propellant rocket for the boost phase and a small turbojet for the sustain phase of the mission, which can extend to a range of 124 miles (200km). The Gabriel Mk IV has the same basic configuration as the Gabriel Mk III with the exception of its wings, which are changed in shape from trapezoidal to swept with cropped tips. The missile has the same guidance options and attack modes as the Gabriel Mk III.

A Norwegian weapon, the Kongsberg Penguin was the Western world's first anti-ship missile, the original Penguin Mk I having been conceived in the early 1960s for a service debut in 1972 as part of Norway's scheme of coastal defence against maritime invasion. This initial model was optimised for good performance in the country's particular coastal waters after launch from fast attack craft and other small naval platforms. The result is a missile with IR terminal homing, treated as a certified round of ammunition, and launched upon information supplied by the launch platform's sensors and fire-control system; this ship-launched version has a two-stage rocket, and height control by an interesting pulsed-laser altimeter. The missile's launch weight is 750lb (340kg) including the powerful warhead essentially identical with the Martin Marietta AGM-12B Bullpup air-to-surface missile, and its performance figures include a range of 12.4 miles (20km). The missiles still in service have been upgraded to Penguin Mk I Mod 7 standard with the seeker of the Penguin Mk II Mod 3. The Penguin Mk II is an improved Mk I with range boosted to 18.6 miles (30km). The type entered service in the early 1980s, and surviving rounds have been upgraded to Penguin Mk II Mod 5 standard with enhanced seeker performance. The basic type has been further developed for helicopter launch as the Penguin Mk II Mod 7 (US designation AGM-119B for use by helicopters such as the Kaman SH-2F Seasprite and Sikorsky SH-60B Seahawk) with a weight of 849lb (385kg). This variant includes a number of Penguin Mk III improvements (notably in the seeker and signal processor), and has a new two-stage rocket motor and fully digital electronics, unlike the earlier Mk II variants, which have analogue electronics. Production of the weapon is undertaken in the USA by Grumman, and the type entered American helicopter-launched service during 1992, although production is thought to have totalled only 82 missiles.

The Penguin Mk III is an air-launched development (also capable of ship launch) intended primarily for use on the Royal Norwegian air force's Lockheed Martin F-16 Fighting Falcon multi-role fighter. The variant, which possesses the alternative designation AGM-119A in the US system, has a longer body, shorter-span wings, a single-stage rocket motor and a radar altimeter. The Penguin Mk III is a highly capable weapon programmed to fly a circuitous approach to the target via one or more waypoints after launch on the basis of radar information from the launch warplane, or through

113

visual sighting with data entered into the missile via the pilot's HUD or optical sight. As with the earlier versions of the missile, the use of IR terminal homing (activated only when the missile has reached the target's anticipated position) gives the target vessel virtually no warning of the missile's imminent arrival, so reducing the time available for countermeasures.

Better known by its combined US and NATO reporting designation AS-2 'Kipper', the K-10 was introduced as the primary Soviet anti-ship weapon of the Tupolev Tu-16 'Badger-C' (one or two such missiles carried semi-recessed under the fuselage) but was also capable of undertaking attacks on large land targets. The K-10 homed on objectives with a large radar signature and, because of its size and lack of electronic sophistication, was completely obsolete by the time of its withdrawal from service in favour of the AS-5 'Kelt'. The type was launched by its parent warplane at a speed of about Mach 0.8 at an altitude of 36,090ft (11,000m), and then accelerated to a high-altitude cruising speed of between Mach 1.4 and Mach 1.5 before descending toward the anticipated target position at about Mach 1.2. The cruise phase of the flight was undertaken under command of an autopilot, which could be overridden and/or updated by data-linked commands from a mid-course guidance aeroplane of the fixed- or rotary-wing type, and then homed on information provided by its onboard active radar seeker. As it was optimised for attacks on targets presenting a large radar signature, this massive missile had as its primary objectives high-value targets such as aircraft carriers. It is worth noting that range estimates for the missile vary considerably from a minimum of 134 miles (215km) to a maximum of 348 miles (560km), although it is likely that the comparative inaccuracy of the guidance system and the desire to maximise the warhead probably dictated a comparatively small fuel capacity and shorter range.

The primary British anti-ship missile, the BAe Sea Eagle was designed from 1976 as the P3T, and the structural and aerodynamic basis of the missile was found in the BAe/Matra Martel missile in service with the British and French air forces and the type to be replaced by the new weapon in the anti-ship role. The origins of the type can be found in the Ministry of Defence's 1973 Air Staff Target 1226, which demanded a weapon possessing considerably greater range than the AJ.168 version of the Martel. The P3T was therefore designed with an air-breathing powerplant in the form of a turbojet aspirated through a ventral inlet whose front was sealed from the airflow by a fairing discarded only after the missile's release from its launch warplane. The missile is otherwise of 'classic' air-launched anti-ship missile configuration, with a cylindrical body terminating forward in the ogival radome for the antenna of the active radar terminal guidance package, a mid-set cruciform of cropped delta wings, and a close-coupled cruciform of cropped delta control fins mounted near the tail and indexed in line with the wings. The Sea Eagle has a thoroughly modern guidance system, and data on the target's position, bearing, course and speed are loaded into this just before the Sea Eagle is launched. After release and engine ignition, the missile

The BAe Sea Eagle is an advanced anti-ship missile used only in its air-launched form. The type has a notably powerful warhead and an advanced guidance package, and achieves long range by the use of a turbojet rather than rocket motor, which allows the whole of the fuel volume to be occupied by liquid fuel (the necessary oxidant being supplied from the air drawn through a ventral inlet) rather than by fuel and oxidant as is necessary for a rocket motor.

accelerates to Mach 0.85 and descends to sea-skimming height under control of its inertial guidance package with height data provided by a radar altimeter: the low-altitude cruise reduces the chances of the missile being spotted by electromagnetic or visual means. The active radar terminal guidance package is activated at a distance of 11 miles (18km) from the target, and the missile then completes its attack. The weapon is controlled via an advanced digital computer, and this allows varying attack heights, the flying of random evasive manoeuvres in the closing stages of the attack, final attack from any bearing, the detection and ignoring of decoys and countermeasures, and on longer-range missions a short climb, when about 18.6 miles (30km) from the target's anticipated position, for use of the active radar to fix the missile's position relative to the target before a descent once again to sea-skimming height. The missile is notable for its good speed and range, and was planned mainly for warplane launch platforms such as the BAe Sea Harrier which can carry two missiles, and also the BAe Buccaneer and Panavia Tornado which can each carry four missiles.

The standard American anti-ship missile is the McDonnell Douglas Harpoon. This is the Western world's most important anti-ship missile, and was conceived in the late 1960s as a capable but comparatively cheap weapon in which reliability rather than outright performance was emphasised in all respects but electronic capability and range. In this last capacity, the use of a turbojet (aspirated via a ventral NACA inlet between the two lower wings) rather than a rocket in the sustainer role pays handsome dividends. In June 1971, McDonnell Douglas received a Department of Defense contract for the full-scale development of this weapon as an air-launched missile, to be carried by the full spectrum of US tactical warplanes for the destruction of surfaced submarines, destroyers, frigates and fast attack craft. It was soon decided that this AGM-84 weapon would be complemented by a ship-launched RGM-84 version, and in 1973 the programme was further enhanced by the addition of the UGM-84 member of the family as an encapsulated version for launch from submerged submarines.

Seven fully guided test launches were completed in June 1974, and the success of this effort was followed by authorisation of pilot production in July 1974 and the start of the US Navy's technical evaluation in October 1974. All three initial variants of the Harpoon missile entered service in 1977 as the AGM-84A air-launched, RGM-84A ship-launched and UGM-84A submarine-launched weapons, the last two having a jettisonable Aerojet booster rocket. The Harpoon is of the standard air-launched anti-ship missile layout, with a cylindrical body terminating forward in the pointed radome over the antenna for the terminal guidance package's active radar, a mid-set cruciform of trapezoidal wings, and a tail-mounted cruciform of swept control fins indexed in line with the wings. Being designed for high-speed air-launch, the AGM-84A requires no booster. This baseline missile can be fired in two modes. The range and bearing launch (RBL) mode allows the late activation of the active radar as a means of reducing the chances of the missile being detected through its own emissions, and in this mode the radar is set for large, medium or small acquisition windows that fix the distance from the anticipated target position at which the radar is activated, although the smaller the acquisition window the more accurate the initial target data must be. The other launch mode is the bearing only launch (BOL), used when the precise location of the target is not available at missile launch time. In this mode the missile is fired on the target's bearing from the launch warplane and the radar is activated comparatively early in the flight to search through 90 degrees (45 degrees left and right of the centreline) in azimuth mode. If no target is found after the low-level approach, the missile undertakes a pre-programmed search pattern and, should this not find a target, the missile self-destructs. Target acquisition is followed in the Block 1A missiles of the initial production batch, typified by a range of 57.6 miles (92.7km), by a steep pop-up climb at a distance of some 2,000yds (1,830m) from the target, and then a terminal dive onto the target's more vulnerable upper surfaces.

The AGM-84B Harpoon was introduced in 1982 as the Block 1B missile that flies a sea-skimming attack, has improved resistance to ECM, and possesses a larger and more devastating warhead. The AGM-84C Harpoon was introduced in 1985 as the Block 1C missile that incorporates the pop-up/terminal dive and sea-skimming flight profile capabilities of the AGM-84A and AGM-84B respectively, together with the latter's larger warhead. The weapon also features an increase in range to more than 121 miles (195km) as a result of its greater fuel capacity and a change from JP-5 to JP-10 fuel, has an improved seeker, and greater computer memory for variable flight profiles including an indirect approach to the target.

The AGM-84D missile would have been a Block 1D development of the Block 1C standard with an advanced version of the current seeker package upgraded with a global positioning system (GPS) receiver, range increased still further to 150 miles (241km) by the carriage of more fuel in a longer body, and the ability to undertake more complex search patterns as well as a dog-leg approach to the target via three waypoints before selection of the more appropriate of the two alternative attack modes, but was cancelled.

Starting trials in 1988 and entering accelerated service during 1990 in time for the UN-led war to free Kuwait from Iraqi occupation, the AGM-84E stand-off land attack missile (SLAM) was developed as a company-funded derivative of the Harpoon for carriage by US Navy and US Marine Corps Northrop Grumman A-6 Intruder and McDonnell Douglas F/A-18 Hornet warplanes. The weapon combines the airframe, powerplant and warhead of the Harpoon with the imaging IR terminal guidance unit of the Hughes AGM-65D Maverick ASM, the data link of the Hughes/Martin Marietta AGM-62 'Walleye' glide bomb, and a GPS receiver, to create a missile that is longer and heavier than the basic Harpoon models. The SLAM provides a stand-off capability against high-value targets such as power stations, harbour equipment and bridges, using inertial guidance for the mid-course phase of the flight before the missile is aligned precisely at the target through the GPS link, allowing the operator to acquire the target up to 10,000yds (9,145m) distant from the missile, lock onto the image and depart the scene as the missile completes its attack. Further development of the SLAM concept could result from McDonnell Douglas's stand-off land attack missile – expanded response (SLAM-ER) proposal that will be evaluated in hardware form towards the end of the present decade with an improved and larger

Seen under this Saab 39 Gripen of the Swedish air force are three important types of air-launched missile, namely the AIM-9 Sidewinder air-to-air missile (wingtip rails), AGM-65 Maverick air-to-surface missile (outboard underwing hardpoints) and Rbs 15 anti-ship missile (inboard underwing hardpoints).

750lb (340kg) warhead, modified wings, and an automated mission-planning capability to improve range to 75 miles (121km).

Air-to-surface missiles fall into two basic categories, as strategic weapons and tactical weapons. The strategic weapons are generally known as cruise missiles. The main French weapon in this category, which is produced by only a very few nations, is the Aérospatiale ASMP (Air-Sol Moyenne Portée, or air-to-surface medium-range missile). Designed from 1978, the ASMP is an air-launched cruise missile now optimised for carriage by the Dassault Mirage IVP bomber (after conversion from Mirage IVA standard), the Dassault Mirage 2000N low-altitude strike warplane and the Dassault Super Etendard carrierborne strike fighter. The ASMP entered service in 1986, and provides the French air forces with a stand-off nuclear capability against large targets such as railway yards, major bridges, and command and communication centres. The type can fly a high-altitude profile ending with a steep supersonic dive, or alternatively a low-altitude profile of shorter range.

The designation AS-15 'Kent' is the US/NATO reporting designation for a cruise missile believed to have the Russian designators Kh-55, Kh-65 and/or RKV-500, and the weapon is the air-launched version of the standard Soviet (now Russian) cruise missile. The missile was developed from the late 1970s in response to the American development of small cruise missiles with folding flying surfaces for minimal containerised storage or aircraft carriage requirements, and with a small turbofan powerplant for maximum range. The weapon is currently operated by the Tupolev Tu-95 'Bear-H' subsonic bomber (six AS-15A 'Kent' missiles in the Tu-95MS-6 on an internal rotary launcher and 16 AS-15A missiles on the Tu-95MS-16 in the form of six missiles internally on a rotary launcher and 10 externally on five two-round pylons) and by the Tupolev Tu-160 'Blackjack' supersonic variable-geometry bomber (12 AS-15B missiles carried internally on two six-round rotary launchers). The AS-15B differs from the AS-15A in its greater diameter, although the significance of this increased fuselage volume has not been discovered. The weapon compares favourably with the USAF's Boeing AGM-86B type, but differs from the American weapon in having land- and sea-based counterparts in the forms of the SS-C-4 and SS-N-21 'Sampson'.

The origins of the cruise missile in Western service can be traced to a time in the early 1950s, when there were serious concerns in Western military circles about the continued viability of the free-fall bomber as the primary weapon for the projection of strategic air power, because the deep penetration of Soviet airspace to drop such nuclear weapons on primary targets left such bombers increasingly vulnerable to interception and destruction. The interception capabilities of turbojet-powered fighters such as the MiG-15 'Fagot' were amply revealed in the Korean War (1950-53), and the transonic performance of such warplanes would soon be exceeded by that of the supersonic fighters that the USSR was known to be developing. The current and foreseeable state of the technological art offered no complete solution to this problem facing the Western powers, and the USA in particular, but the USAF felt that emerging warhead, propulsion and guidance technologies offered the possibility of a partial solution. This partial solution was a large air-to-surface missile carrying a nuclear warhead, guided by an inertial navigation system, and powered by a liquid-propellant rocket motor for supersonic performance and moderately long range.

The USA appreciated that the rocket technology of the day would not provide the range to allow such a missile to be launched from points outside Soviet airspace, but felt that it would offer the type of stand-off launch range that would make it possible for launch warplanes to avoid the heaviest concentrations of Soviet defensive weapons. The first US weapon in this category was the Bell GAM-63 Rascal that saw limited service between 1957 and 1959 with a version of the Boeing B-47 Stratojet medium strategic bomber as its launcher: this DB-47E version carried one 13,500lb (6,124kg) Rascal on a hardpoint on the lower starboard side of the fuselage. The Rascal could carry any of three types of warhead (two of them nuclear), was powered by a liquid-propellant rocket motor for a speed of Mach 1.6 and a range of 75 miles (120km), and used inertial navigation for a CEP in the order of 500yds (457m). The Rascal was a worthy initial effort, but it was appreciated that the type's size and weight reduced range to a wholly indifferent figure.

Even before the Rascal entered service, however, the USAF had decided that a major effort was required to give its Boeing B-52 Stratofortress the ability to penetrate Soviet air defences. This resulted in two parallel programmes: Weapon System 131B was planned as a supersonic missile carrying a thermonuclear warhead, and Weapon System 132B as a supersonic missile carrying an ECM payload. The latter requirement was soon dropped, and after intense industrial competition, the development contract for WS-131B was awarded to the Missile Development Division of North American Aviation in August 1957.

The division was short of work, for its incredible SM-64 Navajo strategic missile had recently been cancelled. The SM-64 was designed to provide the USAF with a missile carrying a large thermonuclear warhead over intercontinental ranges, and had been developed to the point of production as a supersonic cruise missile lifted piggyback fashion by a rocket booster before igniting its own ramjet sustainers for wingborne flight at Mach 3 over a range of 6,333 miles (10,192km.) North American decided that the aerodynamics of the Navajo, or more specifically its X-10 test vehicle, were ideal for the required air-launched cruise missile, and the new type was therefore planned with a very slender fuselage carrying all-moving delta canard foreplane halves for longitudinal control, a rear-mounted delta wing with ailerons for lateral control, and a swept vertical tail surface with an inset rudder for directional control. The powerplant was one Pratt & Whitney J52 turbojet: this was mounted in a nacelle below the fuselage immediately under the rear-mounted wing, and had variable inlet and nozzle systems matching the handling of the non-afterburning engine to flight at up to Mach 2.1 at heights between sea level and 55,000ft (16,765m). Guidance was entrusted to a North American Autonetics inertial system that was primed right up to the point of missile release by the launch warplane's systems, updated by a Kollsman KS-120 astro-tracker located in the missile launch pylon.

The missile was originally designated B-77, but this was changed to GAM-77 and it was with this designation that the first powered test was undertaken in April 1959. The GAM-77 Hound Dog achieved initial

The most important of the USA's early cruise missiles was the North American AGM-28 Hound Dog, which was a nuclear-armed and turbojet-powered winged weapon of which two could be carried by the Boeing B-52 Stratofortress heavy bomber on special underwing pylons (seen attached to the two right-hand weapons ready for rapid connection to the bomber). The range of these inertially guided weapons meant that the bomber no longer had to overfly its target and thereby undergo the threat posed by the target's anti-aircraft guns and surface-to-air missile defences.

operational capability in 1961 on the two underwing pylons of the B-52G Stratofortress, and in 1962 was redesignated as the AGM-28A Hound Dog. Originally designated GAM-77A, the AGM-28B Hound Dog was an improved missile with a number of guidance system refinements as well as the KS-140 astro-tracker in the launch pylon. Production of the Hound Dog lasted to 1963 and encompassed the delivery of 593 missiles.

The launch crew could programme high- or low-altitude flight profiles, including dog-legs and evasive manoeuvres, right up to the point of missile release, whereupon the Hound Dog became entirely autonomous and therefore unjammable. Experiments were undertaken with Hound Dogs converted with anti-radar and terrain comparison or terrain contour matching (TERCOM) guidance, but neither of these types entered operational service before the AGM-28 was withdrawn from service in 1976.

The Boeing AGM-86B entered service in 1981 as one of the USAF's most important weapons. The weapon was originally schemed as the subsonic cruise army decoy (SCAD) to supersede the McDonnell Douglas ADM-20 Quail decoy missile, but was then developed as the long-range complement to the short-range Boeing AGM-69 SRAM, with which it enjoys full launcher compatibility. The warplane for which the new long-range missile was designed was the Rockwell B-1A supersonic bomber and missile launcher, and in its original AGM-86A version the missile was sized in fuselage length to the weapons bay of this important warplane. The B-1A was then cancelled, and the AGM-86A was redesigned as the AGM-86B with a longer fuselage and a wing of reduced sweep, as the primary launch platform was now envisaged as the already venerable Boeing B-52 Stratofortress. The primary launch platform for the weapon in the 1990s is the B-1B Lancer, a radically revised development of the B-1A, that can carry up to 22 such missiles (eight on an internally carried rotary launcher and 14 under the wings), and this penetration bomber is due to be supplemented by the Northrop Grumman B-2A Spirit bomber capable of carrying up to 16 such missiles on two eight-round rotary launchers carried internally, although the preferred cruise missile for this more advanced delivery system is the General Dynamics AGM-129.

Although a total of 4,348 AGM-86Bs was planned, only 1,715 were built between 1982 and 1986, to allow the diversion of funding to the improved

AGM-129 that offered greater capabilities at a time when the Soviets were strengthening their capabilities against air-launched cruise missiles during the mid- and late 1980s. From 1985, in-service rounds were retrofitted with an ECM package to improve their capabilities against such Soviet defences. Designed from 1986 but first revealed in 1991 after its use in the Gulf War, the AGM-86C is the conventionally armed version of the AGM-86B with a 1,000lb (454kg) blast/fragmentation warhead. The greater size of this warhead dictates a reduction in fuel capacity, and hence a reduction in range, but the addition of a GPS receiver considerably enhances terminal accuracy over the already excellent figure for the AGM-86B variant.

It has been suggested that from 1992 the number of AGM-86B missiles in first-line service has been reduced, and that many of these weapons have been revised to the conventionally armed role or the air-launched decoy role with ECM equipment, chaff and IR flares. It has further been suggested that many of the weapons remaining in the nuclear-armed role have been adapted with a bulbous nose containing shielding against electromagnetic pulse effects, and painted with a radar-absorbent coating to reduce their electromagnetic signature.

It is also worth noting that there is a ship- and submarine-launched counterpart to the AGM-86. This General Dynamics BGM-109 Tomahawk was also proposed in air-launched variants and, perhaps most importantly of all, was placed in ground-launched service until withdrawn in the later 1980s as a result of treaty restrictions. The BGM-109 has inertial guidance for the mid-course phase of its flight and either TERCOM or some other guidance package for the terminal phase, and entered service in 1983.

The variants of this important operational- and tactical-level weapon are discussed below in alphabetical order of their variants. The BGM-109A naval variant is also known as the tactical land attack missile – nuclear (TLAM-N), and is a ship- and submarine-launched encapsulated version with the selectable-yield 200-kiloton W80 Model 0 warhead, a range of 1,555 miles (2,500km) and a CEP of 305yds (280m) with inertial and TERCOM guidance.

The BGM-109B Tomahawk is also known as the tactical anti-ship missile (TASM), is designed for ship and submarine launch, and carries a 1,000lb (454kg) HE warhead (derived from that of the AGM-12 Bullpup ASM) over a range of 282 miles (454km). The variant's terminal guidance is provided by an active radar seeker derived from that of the McDonnell Douglas RGM-84A Harpoon anti-ship missile, and this commands the missile into a pop-up/dive attack to strike the target on its vulnerable upper surfaces.

The BGM-109C is also known as the tactical land attack missile – conventional (TLAM-C) and is essentially the airframe of the BGM-109A with the warhead of the BGM-109B and DSW-15(V) DSMAC terminal guidance for great accuracy over a range of 921 miles (1,482km).

The BGM-109D was the variant of the ground-launched Tomahawk cruise missile with Block III

The Martin ASM-N-7 and GAM-83 (from 1962 AGM-12) Bullpup series was the most important air-to-surface missile available to the US Air Force and US Navy in the late 1950s and early 1960s. Seen here are four of the most important members of the family: clockwise from the slim missile (right front) these are the ATM-12A training missile, the AGM-12B, the AGM-12D and the AGM-12C.

improvements and a submunition-dispensing warhead. The type was powered by a version of the F402 turbofan offering 19 per cent greater thrust at 2 per cent less fuel consumption, and other improvements included the Mk IIA version of the DSMAC guidance package.

The BGM-109G Tomahawk was known as the ground-launched cruise missile (GLCM) and was the strategic version of the series deployed extensively in Europe in the theatre-level nuclear role. The weapon was carried in a high-mobility four-round TEL vehicle designed for rapid deployment (in times of crisis and war) away from Soviet-targeted base areas. A group of four TELs was supported by two wheeled launch control centres to provide launch and targeting data, and to provide the crews with nuclear, biological and chemical (NBC) protection.

The AGM-109H Tomahawk was the proposed medium-range air-launched airfield attack cruise missile for the USAF with the Teledyne Continental J402-CA-401 engine and a conventional warhead with tactical submunition payload. The AGM-109K Tomahawk was the proposed medium-range air-launched land attack and sea lane control cruise missile for the USAF with the J402-CA-401 engine and the WDU-25A/B conventional warhead. The AGM-109L Tomahawk was the proposed medium-range air-launched land/sea attack cruise missile for the US Navy with the J402-CA-401 engine and the WDU-7B conventional warhead.

The General Dynamics AGM-129A is an important weapon that entered service in 1991, but very little is known of its highly classified development. The programme to develop this successor to the Boeing AGM-86B air-launched cruise missile was launched in 1977 with the object of improving performance in several crucial fields. Low observability was required for an increased capability to penetrate into airspace protected by advanced air defences, and led to the development and introduction of 'stealth' technology. Improved propulsion was demanded through the installation of an engine offering greater power at lower specific fuel consumption for the greater range that would allow the missile to circumnavigate the most heavily defended areas of Soviet (now Russian) airspace. Greater survivability was desired for better operational capability, and was provided through the incorporation of the most advanced electronic and IR countermeasures. Finally, enhanced targeting flexibility and terminal accuracy were important improvements that were generated by use of the latest computer hardware and software.

The fact that development of the AGM had been awarded to General Dynamics was announced in 1983 when full-scale development began, and the type was designed for use on the Boeing B-52 Stratofortress, with the Rockwell B-1B Lancer and Northrop Grumman B-2A Spirit bombers later becoming operational with the type. Key features are longer range than the AGM-86B combined with a high measure of 'stealth' technology (especially in terms of IR emission) to reduce the missile's observability. The type has a flattened fuselage shape with a pointed wedge nose and a flat wedge tail section, and the folding aerodynamic surfaces comprise forward-swept wings on the central part of the fuselage and at the tail a combination of an unswept tailplane and a swept ventral fin, all of the tail surfaces being of the 'slab' or all-moving type. The whole design, probably making extensive use of composite materials, was optimised for low observability, and the same can be said of the powerplant, which has a low thermal signature and is aspirated via a flush ventral inlet and exhausts through a two-dimensional slot beneath the missile's upswept tail. The missile's low detectability by radar is ensured by the careful design of the nose and upper surfaces, reflecting the fact that the most likely detectors will be those above and ahead of the missile: the nose accommodates on its undersurface the conformal antenna for the laser radar associated with the primary guidance system, while the inlet, exhaust and rudder are all shielded by the missile's afterbody. Production of 1,461 such missiles was planned but, reflecting the effective collapse of the USSR in the late 1980s, the programme was terminated in 1993 after the delivery of just 460 missiles.

Under development in the mid-1990s for possible production by Hughes (originally General Dynamics) and McDonnell Douglas, which was qualified as second-source manufacturer during 1987, the AGM-129B is a derivative of the AGM-129A with a conventional warhead or, according to some sources, provision for the carriage of advanced submunitions.

The Hughes AIM-4 Falcon was the world's first fully guided air-to-air (AAM) to enter operational service, an event that took place in 1956. The origins of this weapon can be traced to 1947, when the USAF demanded the creation of a sophisticated combination of radar fire-control system and

The single most important designer and manufacturer of air-launched missiles in the USA is Hughes, and among this company's series of such weapons are the BGM-71 TOW surface- and helicopter-launched anti-tank missile (foreground) and (background left to right) the AIM-47A Super Falcon air-to-air missile, the AIM-4F Falcon air-to-air missile, the AIM-26A Super Falcon, the AGM-65 Maverick air-to-surface missile, the AIM-4D Falcon air-to-air missile, and the AIM-54A Phoenix air-to-air missile.

guided missile for installation in the high-performance manned interceptors that the service considered to be the only satisfactory weapon for the defence of the continental USA against the possible depredations of bombers carrying free-fall nuclear bombs. The resulting competition drew responses from most American electronics and aircraft manufacturers, but all of these were surprised when the decisions for the fire-control and missile systems were made in favour of Hughes Aircraft, a newcomer in this highly advanced field.

The first fire-control system to emerge from Hughes' victory in the design competition was the E-9 installed in the Northrop F-89H Scorpion all-weather fighter, and this was followed by the MG-10 for the Convair F-102 Delta Dagger supersonic interceptor, the MG-13 for the McDonnell F-101 Voodoo supersonic interceptor, and the MA-1 for the Convair F-106 Delta Dart Mach 2 interceptor. All these systems were designed for use with a single AAM type, which resulted from Project 'Dragonfly' and was ordered in 1947 as the XF-98 in the fighter category, before becoming the GAR-1 Falcon in the new guided missile system during 1950, and finally the AIM-4 Falcon in the 1962 rationalisation of the designation systems.

The missile established a basic configuration that has been typical of Hughes missiles since that time: a cylindrical body of comparatively great diameter with a hemispherical nose and a large proportion of composites (in this instance glassfibre-reinforced plastics), and a cruciform of low-aspect-ratio delta flying surfaces each trailed by a rectangular elevon for aerodynamic control of the missile's flight. In the GAR-1, the nose was fitted with four receiver antennae (shaped like small fins and spaced at 90 degrees to each other) giving proportional navigation capability to the semi-active radar guidance system, and propulsion was entrusted to a single-charge rocket motor that boosted the missile at about 50 g until motor burn-out. The GAR-1 reached full service in 1956 on the F-89H/J (three missiles in each of the two wing-tip pods) and F-102A (six missiles in the lower-fuselage weapon bay).

Introduced after the GAR-2 (from 1962 AIM-4B) and known until 1962 as the GAR-1D, this model had control surfaces of greater area moved farther to the rear of the missile's centre of gravity, and a result was enhanced manoeuvrability. The same type of semi-active radar guidance was employed in this model.

Introduced late in 1956 as the second operational Falcon model, the AIM-4B was known until 1962 as the GAR-2 and introduced IR guidance with its seeker in a glazed nose. Known until 1962 as the GAR-2A, the AIM-4C was the second IR-guided version to enter service, and was in essence an improved GAR-2 with an upgraded seeker able to lock onto its target against a wider range of background temperatures.

Ordered as the GAR-2B but entering service in 1963 as the AIM-4D after the tri-service rationalisation of US designation systems, this was the last production version of the Falcon, produced to the extent of more than 12,000 weapons in the form of 4,000 new-build weapons and more than 8,000 remanufactured from surplus AIM-4A and AIM-4C missiles. The type was carried mainly by the F-106A Delta Dart, and was the only Falcon variant optimised for the air-combat role. A hybrid model, the AIM-4D combined the small airframe of the early Falcon models with the more powerful rocket motor and advanced IR seeker of the larger AIM-4G Falcon to create a comparatively short-ranged but very fast missile that otherwise differed from the AIM-4C only in its maximum speed of Mach 4.

Known as the GAR-3 when it entered service in 1958 and built to the extent of just 300 missiles, the AIM-4E Super Falcon was a special high-performance variant of the basic Falcon family, optimised for compatibility with the F-106A Delta Dart with a larger airframe supporting a longer-burning rocket motor, a cruciform wing arrangement with long root fillets, a more powerful warhead, and an improved semi-active radar homing system using an antenna under a pointed radome. In respect of its dimensions, weight and performance, the AIM-4E was basically similar to the AIM-4F. Introduced in 1959 as the GAR-3A, the AIM-4F Super Falcon was a much-improved model matched to the F-106A Delta Dart interceptor and based on the airframe introduced in the GAR-3A but fitted with a two-stage rocket motor and an improved guidance package offering greater accuracy and improved ECM capability. Also introduced in 1959 with the initial designation GAR-4A, the AIM-4G Super Falcon was a version of the AIM-4F with IR guidance capable of locking onto smaller targets at longer ranges. The last development of the Falcon series was the XAIM-4H, evolved between 1969 and the programme's termination in 1971 with an active laser fuse system, and the last of the Falcon series in operational service were the models in Swedish and Swiss service up to the early 1990s.

In 1946 the US Navy's Bureau of Aeronautics was convinced that the guided AAM was the way forward in fighter armament, and contracted with Sperry Gyroscope for initial conceptual work within the context of Project 'Hot Shot'. By 1951, Sperry had made sufficient progress for the US Navy to contract for full engineering development of the AAM-N-2 Sparrow I (redesignated as the AIM-7A in 1962). The Sparrow I made its first flight in 1953, based on a long and slender body with a pointed nose carrying the 52lb (23.6kg) proximity-fused blast/fragmentation warhead, an Aerojet solid-propellant rocket motor, and flying surfaces that included a cruciform of moving wings located on the body's mid-point and, indexed in line with these wings, a cruciform of fixed fins at the tail. This model used radar beam-riding guidance with flush dipole antennae round the body to detect the missile's position in the beam stretching from the launch fighter to the target, and thus provided the data with which the guidance system could keep the missile centred in the beam by movement of the control wings.

The AAM-N-2 reached initial operational capability in July 1956, and about 2,000 such missiles were produced for fighters such as the Douglas F3D-2M Skyknight, McDonnell F3H-2M Demon and Vought F7U-3M Cutlass, each of which could carry four missiles under their wings. In 1955, Douglas was developing for the US Navy the F5D-1 Skylancer as a Mach 2 interceptor with the Westinghouse Aero X-24A target-acquisition and fire-control radar, and decided that a much-improved version of the Sparrow would make ideal armament for this advanced type. In that year, therefore, the company received a US Navy contract for the AAM-N-3 Sparrow II AAM to arm the Skylancer. Douglas concentrated on aerodynamic and structural development of the missile on the basis of the Sparrow I, and contracted parallel development of the all-important missile guidance package to Bendix-Pacific. The logical choice of guidance type would have been semi-active radar homing, but the design team opted instead to design and develop a far more ambitious active radar guidance, despite the considerable problems posed by the missile's diameter of only 8in (0.203m). The body was given greater volume, especially in its forward portion, and the flying surfaces were given square-cut tips. About 100 missiles, which received the retrospective designation AIM-7B Sparrow II in 1962, were produced for test and development work, but in 1956 the US Navy cancelled both the Skylancer and the Sparrow II as more advanced fighter/missile combinations were imminent.

When production of the Sparrow I ended in 1956, Raytheon took over the Naval Reserve Plant at Bristol, Tennessee, previously operated by the

Farragut Division of Sperry Gyroscope. Here the new prime contractor set about the creation of the Sparrow III as a derivative of the Sparrow II with semi-active radar guidance. The body was of precision-cast light alloy and accommodated, from nose to tail, the guidance package based on the novel continuous-wave semi-active radar homing system, the autopilot and the motors for the cruciform arrangement of moving control wings, the blast/fragmentation warhead behind the wings, and the Aerojet rocket motor whose solid propellant was not cast integrally with the case. This created the AAM-N-6 Sparrow III that entered service during 1958 on the F3H-3M Demon and became the AIM-7C in 1962. This initial Sparrow III had the same dimensions as its later derivatives, but weighed 380lb (172.4kg) and was capable of reaching a range of 25 miles (40km). The missile was designed for the medium-range engagement of non-manoeuvring targets.

Initially accepted for service with the US Navy as the AAM-N-6A Sparrow III and with the USAF as the AIM-101 Sparrow III before both models received the revised designation AIM-7D in 1962, this was an improved version of the AAM-N-6 with a Thiokol (Reaction Motors) pre-packaged liquid-propellant rocket motor that raised weight to 440lb (200kg).

Introduced in 1962 as the AAM-N-6B Sparrow III, the AIM-7E was the first member of the Sparrow family to enter large-scale production: 25,000 missiles were built, and the variant remains in limited service with several important fighter types. The type is powered by a Rocketdyne Mk 38 Model 2 (later Aerojet Mk 52) single-stage rocket motor for a burn-out speed of Mach 3.7 and range of 28 miles (44km), and weighs 452lb (205kg) with its revised 66lb (29.9kg) continuous rod blast/fragmentation warhead whose casing breaks into some 2,600 fragments on detonation. The weapon uses Raytheon continuous-wave semi-active radar guidance matched to a number of radars such as the Rockwell R21G/H (Aeritalia F-104S), APQ-72, APQ-100, APQ-109, APQ-120 and APG-59 (F-4 Phantom II) and AWG-9 (Grumman F-14 Tomcat). This variant was also built in Japan by Mitsubishi as the AIM-7EJ Sparrow III and in Italy by Selenia, and a limited-production

The latest Hughes air-to-air missile is the AIM-120 advanced medium-range air-to-air missile (AMRAAM), which was designed to provide the same range and lethality as the AIM-7 Sparrow air-to-air missile, with semi-active radar guidance in a package of little more than the size of the AIM-9 Sidewinder short-range air-to-air missile, together with advanced features such as a combination of inertial and active radar guidance for the mid-course and terminal phases of the flight respectively.

shorter-range and more manoeuvrable version was produced in the USA as the AIM-7E2 Sparrow III.

This last version was developed in response to a requirement that became apparent in the Vietnam War, in which US fighters were seldom able to use the long-range AIM-7E because of the political ban on firing missiles against aircraft that had not been identified visually; on the few occasions when pilots were able to fire their early-generation Sparrow IIIs, they found these initial models to be virtually useless against manoeuvring targets at shorter ranges. The AIM-7E2 was therefore developed with a reduced minimum range and enhanced manoeuvrability, the latter being provided by higher-powered hydraulic controls for its cruciform of moving wings; the opportunity was also taken to provide aerodynamic surfaces that could be plugged in rather than attached with the aid of special tools. The definitive version still in limited and declining service is the AIM-7E3 Sparrow III, which is a conversion of the AIM-7E2 with improved reliability and greater target-sensing capability. Further refined models, thought to remain in only very limited service up to the early 1990s, were the AIM-7E4 Sparrow III and AIM-7E6 Sparrow III.

The AIM-7F Sparrow III is a redesigned version for use on the McDonnell Douglas F-15 Eagle and now carried also by the McDonnell Douglas F/A-18 Hornet. The variant was introduced in 1977, and was built by Raytheon with the Pomona Division of General Dynamics (now Hughes Missile Systems) brought into the programme as the second-source manufacturer. Whereas the AIM-7E has the forward part of its body filled with guidance equipment (homing head and autopilot) and the rear part aft of the wings occupied by a comparatively small warhead and a short rocket motor, the AIM-7F uses the advantages of more compact solid-state electronics to reduce guidance package volume by some 40 per cent, allowing a larger warhead to be incorporated in the space vacated in front of the wings, and a longer motor to be used in the whole of the portion aft of the wings. The variant therefore has a much larger engagement envelope through the adoption of solid-state electronics and a Mk 58 or Mk 65 dual-thrust rocket motor for a range of 62 miles (100km). The AIM-7F is dimensionally identical with the AIM-7E, but weighs 503lb (228kg) and has

Built in larger numbers than any other missile and over a longer production period, the AIM-9 Sidewinder is still the most important short-range air-to-air missile in the inventory of the USA and its allies. The type was initially limited to basic pursuit-course engagements at very short ranges and under ideal optical conditions, but has since been developed into a considerably more versatile weapon with an all-aspect engagement capability together with longer range and considerable dogfighting agility for the tackling of manoeuvring targets.

an 88lb (39.9kg) Mk 71 continuous rod blast/fragmentation warhead. The use of continuous-wave and pulse-Doppler guidance with a conical-scan slotted antenna considerably enhances 'look-down/shoot-down' capability, even at the longer ranges possible with the variant, and the AIM-7F also possesses superior ECM resistance.

Introduced in 1982 as an interim type pending availability of the Hughes AIM-120 advanced medium-range AAM (AMRAAM), the AIM-7M Sparrow III has a new digital monopulse seeker that was selected in preference to a General Dynamics seeker developed initially for the Standard 2 naval SAM. The chosen seeker offers performance comparable with the Marconi unit in the British Sky Flash derivative, especially in the longer-range look-down/shoot-down mode. The variant also offers other electronic and engineering improvements to bring down production cost while enhancing reliability and performance at low altitude and in ECM environments.

Developed in the late 1980s by Raytheon, the AIM-7P Sparrow III is the latest evolution of the basic Sparrow III AAM. Few details of the programme have been released, but it is known that the development is centred on electronic rather than aerodynamic or powerplant features, and is based on improved guidance electronics, a new fuse, an onboard computer using very high speed integrated circuit (VHSIC) technology for twice the data capacity and handling speed of the current model, and the ability to receive mid-course guidance updates from the launch warplane. The AIM-7P entered service in 1992, and possesses the same dimensions, weights and performance as the AIM-7M.

In 1991 a contract was issued to Iriss (a joint-venture company created by Raytheon and General Dynamics) for the development of an IR seeker suitable for installation in the Sparrow III AAM and the RIM-67A Standard 2 SAM, providing these two weapons with a passive homing system as an alternative to their semi-active radar homing system. The practical result of this programme is the AIM-7R Sparrow III, which has, on the tip of its semi-active radar antenna's radome, an IR seeker derived from that of the AIM-9 Sidewinder. This additional seeker unit is cooled by compressed gas carried in the body of the missile. On launch, the missile activates the IR seeker to undertake its standard search routine: if the IR seeker acquires and locks onto a target, the rest of the engagement is flown with IR guidance; if the IR seeker fails to acquire or lock onto a target, or if target lock is subsequently lost, the semi-active radar guidance package is activated and assumes the primary guidance role unless the reactivated IR seeker again acquires the target. The AIM-7R is scheduled to enter service later in the current decade, and possesses the same dimensions, weights and performance as the AIM-7M.

The short-range partner to the medium-range AIM-7 Sparrow has been the AIM-9 Sidewinder, a truly remarkable weapon designed under the aegis of the US Navy and built to the extent of 200,000 or more examples in a programme that is still witnessing the active development of this seminally important type. Convinced that one of the keys to air-combat success with jet-powered fighters would be the replacement of the four standard 20mm cannon by the fully guided missile, the US Navy decided in the late 1940s to set in hand, at one of its own establishments, the creation of a simple AAM. The establishment selected was the Naval Ordnance Test Station (later Naval Weapons Center) at China Lake, California, and in 1949 work started on a novel weapon that would be cheap to make, simple to use but wholly effective in operation.

The success of the NOTS team is attested by the fact that its missile is still in development well as production and service, and has been built in larger numbers than any other AAM in history, with the possible exception

127

of the R-3 (AA-2 'Atoll'), a Soviet weapon that was developed from the American weapon. The NOTS team decided to base its design on a body fabricated from aluminium tubing with a diameter of only 5in (0.127m), and carrying a passive seeker working on IR principles. NOTS developed the basic concept for this IR seeker despite the difficulties of installing vacuum-tube electronics in so slender a body, and in 1951 Philco (later Philco-Ford) was awarded the contract to develop this basic research into a practical seeker unit for the missile's production models. From front to rear, the missile carried the seeker head and associated guidance package, the cruciform of moving control fins, the annular blast/fragmentation warhead, the solid-propellant rocket motor and, round the motor's exhaust, a cruciform of fixed fins indexed in line with the control fins. The tip of each fixed fin's trailing edge carried a slipstream-driven 'rolleron' whose gyroscopic action helped to stabilize the missile in flight.

The missile's powerplant was designed by the Naval Propellant Plant but built for production weapons by Hercules, Hunter-Douglas and Norris-Thermador: this unit boosted the missile to Mach 2.5 in its burn time of 2.2 seconds. The seeker was based on an uncooled lead sulphide sensor with a target-acquisition angle of 25 degrees, a seeker field of vision of 4 degrees and a tracking rate of 11 degrees per second, and trials (from the first fully guided test firing in September 1953) confirmed that the seeker and guidance package could indeed produce a 70 per cent single-shot kill probability. The trials also confirmed, however, that this percentage could only be achieved in a high-altitude pursuit engagement in good optical conditions, and that the percentage fell dramatically at lower altitudes, in poor optical conditions (including cloud and rain), and whenever the seeker was offered the chance to lock onto tempting alternative targets such as the sun, bright sky or even reflections in lakes and rivers. Even so, the Sidewinder was clearly a usable weapon by the standards of the day, and it was obvious that the basic concept had only just started to explore the capabilities inherent in the new technology embodied in its seeker. The utility of the Sidewinder was increased by its light weight, basic simplicity (it was claimed that the weapon carried less than 25 moving parts) and independence from any targeting system other than the pilot's eyes. This meant that virtually any fighter capable of lifting the weapon as an external load could be equipped with the Sidewinder.

All the pilot had to do was acquire a target optically, fly straight towards it until his fighter was within launch range, activate the missile, listen in his headset as the low-pitched growl of the seeker rose to a high-pitched whine indicating that the target had been acquired by the seeker and locked into the missile's seeker/guidance system, and then launched the weapon. The missile was thus a fire-and-forget weapon, and this had the important tactical advantage of permitting the pilot to turn his fighter away from the target as soon as a missile had been launched.

Designed for the abortive General Dynamics F-111B swing-wing naval fighter, the Hughes AIM-54 Phoenix long-range AAM was brought to fruition (together with its associated Hughes AWG-9 pulse-Doppler radar fire-control system) in the Grumman F-14 Tomcat fleet-defence fighter. In 1957 the US Navy had issued a request for proposals for a new fighter/missile combination that would provide its carrier battle groups with the aerial means to carry "the entire burden of effecting the interception" of inbound hostile warplanes at long range from their American targets. The warplane designed to meet this need was the Douglas F6D Missileer, which was planned as a completely subsonic launch platform for six long-range AAMs. The sole function of the Missileer was to patrol at an altitude of

Seen here in prototype form, the Hughes AIM-54 is the Western world's longest-ranged air-to-air missile, and is a truly formidable weapon providing the Northrop Grumman F-14 Tomcat carrierborne fighters of the US Navy with the ability to deal with nuclear-armed aircraft and even missiles at significant range from the carrier battle group under threat.

35,000ft (10,670m) and at a radius of 150 miles (241km) from its parent carrier, and use its powerful Westinghouse APQ-81 track-while-scan radar to detect and track hostile warplanes at the maximum possible range, and then launch the requisite number of AAMs to home on the targets using their own active radar guidance.

The missile selected for development was the Grumman/Bendix AAM-N-10 Eagle, at that time the largest AAM planned anywhere in the world. The missile was based on a two-stage layout at a maximum weight of 1,284lb (582kg) and an overall length of 16ft 1.5in (4.91m), and was designed to cruise at Mach 4 over a maximum range of 127 miles (204km).

There was considerable political antipathy to a 'fighter' as slow as the Missileer, however, and the fact that the warplane was a launch platform rather than a fighter was not allowed to intervene in the December 1960 decision to cancel the Missileer. The Eagle programme was allowed to continued for a short while to provide technical data for the new missile that was now needed, and which would be carried by the F-111B selected in place of the Missileer. The new AAM was required to match the AWG-9 pulse-Doppler radar and associated fire-control system (derived from the ASQ-18 system of the Lockheed YF-12A experimental fighter), which was intended to detect targets under look-down conditions at a range of more than 150 miles (241 km). Another AAM of the period was the Hughes GAR-9 (AIM-47A from 1962), designed as a radical development of the Falcon series to arm the USAF's North American F-108 Rapier Mach 3 interceptor: this warplane was cancelled, but the GAR-9 was carried on an experimental basis by the YF-12A.

Hughes began work on its AAM-N-11 naval missile contender in 1960, and was able to draw on data from the AAM-N-10 and GAR-9 programmes.

The design team decided to retain the classic aerodynamics of Hughes' earlier AAMs: a substantial body therefore carried on its rear portion a cruciform of low-aspect-ratio delta wings trailed by rectangular control surfaces indexed in line with the wings. The considerable body diameter allowed the use of a wide planar-array radar antenna behind the nose radome, and also provided volume for the missile's other primary components which were, from front to rear, the electronics (radar, guidance package and radar proximity fuse system), the large warhead, the solid-propellant rocket and, round this motor's nozzle, the autopilot and hydraulically powered actuators for the control surfaces.

By then redesignated AIM-54 Phoenix, the missile made its first test flight in 1965 and soon proved itself to possess exceptional capabilities. The standard flight profile flown by the Phoenix starts with a post-launch climb to a peak altitude of 81,400ft (24,810m), where the missile cruises under control of the onboard autopilot with guidance of the semi-active type using reflections from the target of the radar in the launch warplane's AWG-9 system. This high-altitude cruise maximises range by reducing drag and providing the rocket motor with optimum operating conditions, and as the missile finally dives down to the attack the energy potential of the cruise altitude is converted into kinetic energy for greater manoeuvrability in the terminal phase of the flight. The missile's radar switches to the active mode for the final 20,000yds (18,290m) of the attack, the availability of three fusing modes offering maximum target-destruction capability.

The Phoenix entered service in 1974 as the AIM-54A, and notable features of the missile and fire-control combination include exceptional range, and the ability to engage six targets simultaneously (using a time-share system so that the AWG-9 can control the missiles, which can lose touch with the radar for 14 seconds before failing to re-acquire the designated target) regardless of weather conditions and target aspect. Production continued up to 1980, by which time some 2,566 AIM-54A and AIM-54B rounds had been made.

The AIM-54B Phoenix version entered production in late 1977, and is in essence a product-improved AIM-54A with sheet-metal rather than honeycomb aerodynamic surfaces, non-liquid hydraulic and thermal-conditioning systems, and a degree of simplified engineering to ease production.

Developed from 1977 and introduced to production and service in 1982 and 1985 respectively, the AIM-54C Phoenix is a considerably improved missile with digital rather than analogue electronics, a new Nortronics strapdown inertial reference unit, solid-state radar, eight internal rather than four semi-external radar proximity fuse antennae, and more-capable electronic counter-countermeasures (ECCM). This variant weighs 1,008lb (457kg), and its other data include a speed of Mach 5 and a ceiling of more than 100,000ft (30,490m). As with the AIM-54A, legend range has been considerably exceeded in service, especially when the F-14 launch warplane is supported by a Grumman E-2C Hawkeye airborne early warning and control system platform.

Developed under the designation AIM-54C (Sealed), the AIM-54C+ Phoenix is the definitive AIM-54 variant for the F-14D variant of the Tomcat fighter. The new model has a self-contained closed-cycle cooling system (to obviate some of the aerodynamic restrictions imposed on earlier variants by

The AIM-7 Sparrow air-to-air missile was the most important of the American-designed missiles used between the 1960s and mid-1980s for the medium-range role, and was designed to provide fighters such as the McDonnell Douglas F-4 Phantom with the ability to tackle targets under beyond visual range (BVR) conditions. These are examples of the AIM-7F variant.

aerodynamic heating) and improved ECCM capability. Production of the AIM-54C ended in 1993 after the delivery of some 2,000 missiles.

Currently one of the most important American air-launched weapons, the Hughes AIM-120 AMRAAM resulted from the US forces' appreciation by the mid-1970s that the Raytheon AIM-7F Sparrow III medium-range AAM was obsolescent in its intended role of BVR (beyond visual range) engagements of high-value targets. As the two primary warplane-operating services, the USAF and US Navy decided that it made technical as well as financial sense to combine their needs into a requirement for a single type that was interchangeable not only with the Sparrow III but also with the smaller and lighter Ford/Raytheon AIM-9 Sidewinder. The requirement called for an advanced weapon providing considerably higher performance and lethality than any conceivable Sparrow III development, within the context of an aerodynamic and structural package that was also to be cheaper, more reliable, smaller and lighter than the Sparrow III.

Although the new missile was required to replace the Sparrow III on existing fighters, it was also planned with later warplanes in mind. These fighters would be fitted with advanced pulse-Doppler radar equipments using prtogrammeable signal processors for the type of beam sharpening that can provide active but accurate target detection at long range, and also with IR sensors for passive but less accurate target detection at slightly shorter ranges. This opened the way for the AAM to be launched at the upper end of the medium-range bracket without any lock onto the target.

The engagement sequence therefore calls for the pilot of the launch warplane to acquire and track the target, an onboard computer meanwhile calculating the launch acceptability zones and displaying this information to the pilot. The pilot then decides to launch a missile, and inertial reference data on the launch warplane and the target are then loaded into the missile's computer to provide initial navigation information. Once it has been fired, the missile flies the mid-course phase of its flight under control of its strapdown INS, using both the guidance laws stored in its own computer and reference data supplied from the launch warplane's computer to fly the missile to the three-dimensional point previously calculated to put the missile in active seeker range of its target. During this phase of the missile's flight, the pilot of the launch warplane continues to track the target until the moment the missile's active seeker is activated, and he is then free to break away. Once its active seeker has been turned on, the missile acquires and tracks the target, the onboard computer controlling the terminal phase of the flight. As the missile acquires its target with its own active seeker (which also has a 'home-on-jam' mode), only in the last stage of its high-speed flight, the target thus receives minimal warning of the impending attack and has very little time to counter its attacker.

Five industrial groupings competed for the AMRAAM's development contract, but by February 1979 these had been reduced to two, and in late 1981 Hughes was selected as winner over Raytheon. Hughes was contracted to build 94 test missiles with options for another 924 initial-production weapons at the beginning of a programme planned to total at least 20,000 missiles produced by Hughes and a second-source manufacturer, as which Raytheon was later selected. The programme was seen as complementary to that being considered for an advanced short-range air-to-air missile (ASRAAM) to succeed the Ford AIM-9 Sidewinder. Both efforts were understood to have NATO applications, and during August 1980 the UK, USA and West Germany signed a memorandum of understanding for the USA to develop the AMRAAM while the two European countries concentrated on the collaborative development of the ASRAAM. The whole AMRAAM project, which envisaged a missile with size and weight little more than that of the Sidewinder, and with capabilities and performance better than those of the larger Sparrow, was bedevilled during its development period by technical problems, slipping schedules, cost overruns and political antipathy, while pilot production missiles revealed an unacceptably low level of reliability and maintainability.

Thus it was only in 1992 that the AIM-120A finally entered full-scale production within the context of a programme that envisaged the delivery of 13,000 or more missiles for the USAF and US Navy, which accepted the type in 1991 and 1993 respectively.

The missile deviates from the basic configuration used in all previous missiles from the Hughes stable, for it resembles the Sparrow III in its layout: a slender body carries the radar and associated guidance system in its forward portion, the central and rear portions are occupied by the warhead and rocket motor, and the flying surfaces comprise a mid-set cruciform of fixed delta wings and, indexed in line with these surfaces, a cruciform of cropped delta moving tail fins.

With most of its technical problems solved, the AMRAAM offers far greater lethality than even the AIM-7M/P/R variants of the Sparrow III, and among its other advantages are increased speed and range, reduced smoke emission, superior guidance and ECCM capabilities, a more potent warhead with a more effective fusing system, and the ability to be installed on hardpoints previously capable of accepting only the lightweight Sidewinder. US production of the AIM-120A ended in December 1994 after delivery of some 4,000 such missiles.

Entering production in 1994, the AIM-120B AMRAAM is a development of the AIM-120A with a more advanced active radar guidance package incorporating a reprogrammeable signal processor that considerably enhances the missile's tactical versatility. Designed from 1993 and due to enter service in 1997, the AIM-120C AMRAAM further-enhanced missile is the result of Phase 1 of the AMRAAM P3I (Pre-Planned Product Improvement) programme, and its two major differences from the AIM-120A/B are flying surfaces of reduced span to allow internal carriage by the Lockheed Martin/Boeing F-22 Rapier advanced tactical fighter, and an ECCM subsystem that can be reprogrammed for greater operational flexibility in the face of any evolving threat. The Phase 2 development is later expected to add an aimable warhead, an improved fuse, and an updated safety and arming unit, while the Phase 3 development planned for the longer term could include propulsion by a rocket/ramjet unit installed in a body of composite construction for greater speed and range.

The United States also leads the field in SAMs, and a brief survey of some of that country's most important weapons indicates the 'current state of the art' in shoulder-launched short-range and land-mobile medium-range weapons, with a British

The FIM-43 Redeye was the world's first operational shoulder-launched surface-to-air missile. It is therefore of seminal importance in the development of weapons to provide infantry units with a measure of organic capability against attack aircraft of both the fixed- and rotary-wing types. As might be expected of a first-generation weapon of this type, the weapon was decidedly limited in capability; being limited to pursuit-course interceptions, to engage targets only after they that delivered their ordnance and were departing the scene.

system serving as a good example of the type of battlefield weapon currently in service for tasks such as defence against attack helicopters.

When it entered service in 1964, the General Dynamics FIM-43 Redeye provided the US forces with a new breed of air-defence weapon, as it was the world's first man-portable SAM system to reach operational status, and the Redeye was produced in substantial numbers. Yet it was clear from the type's infancy in service that the weapon possessed severe tactical limitations: the operating frequency of its IR seeker was matched to hot metal (in fact the temperature of a typical jetpipe), and its performance in speed and range was low. This meant that the Redeye was limited to the pursuit-course engagement of warplanes that had already delivered their weapons, while the missile's indifferent flight performance meant that successful interception of all but slow and non-manoeuvring targets was very unlikely. Throughout the 1960s, General Dynamics' Pomona Division worked closely with the US Army and US Marine Corps in formulating the tactical and technical specification for a 'Redeye II' missile system, and then in evolving the technologies required for this considerably improved weapon. Naturally enough, the requirement was centred on a radically improved seeker unit offering a virtually total all-aspect engagement capability, and on a superior rocket motor for considerably enhanced performance so that pursuit-course engagements of high-performance warplanes could be undertaken.

By the early 1970s it was believed that the technology had matured adequately for development of the 'Redeye II' to begin. By this time the missile was sufficiently different from the original Redeye and received a wholly different designation, and when General Dynamics was awarded a full engineering development contract in July 1972, the missile became the FIM-92 Stinger. The primary design features of the Stinger were the new Atlantic Research dual-thrust rocket motor, using advanced propellants to ensure performance levels appreciably higher than those of the Redeye despite the Stinger's greater weight, and the considerably more capable IR seeker, with a frequency matched to that of the exhaust plume rather than hot metal. This latter feature offered a significantly expanded acquisition envelope, the only genuinely 'dead' spot being the head-on angle. Other major and important improvements over the Redeye were the incorporation of an integral identification friend or foe (IFF) system (to allow launch before positive visual identification of high-performance targets) and greater resistance to countermeasures of the electronic and IR varieties.

The Stinger emerged as a slim weapon based on a cylindrical body with an untapered nose section and tapered tail section. The former has a hemispherical nose transparency over the seeker, followed by the fuse system, guidance and control electronics (from which the cruciform of rectangular control surfaces springs out as the missile leaves its launch tube), and warhead that terminates in the rocket nozzle and modestly swept cruciform of fixed fins indexed in line with the control surfaces.

Like the Redeye, the Stinger is delivered as a certified round of ammunition in its own container/launcher. This allows the missile to be transported in a manner least likely to result in physical damage, and keeps the weapon under optimum humidity conditions to prevent electronic damage. The missile is further protected by use of a carrying container for the complete system (containerised missile, gripstock assembly, IFF unit, and battery/coolant unit). In action the containerised missile, the firing unit/gripstock, IFF subsystem and battery/coolant unit have merely to be joined together in a process that completes all the electrical connections required. The operator then acquires his target visually in the system's open sight, which projects upwards and to the left from the gripstock to a point in front of the operator's right eye, and interrogates it with his belt-mounted IFF subsystem (claimed to be the smallest such unit in the world) whose antennae are plate-like units to the right of the gripstock.

If an unacceptable IFF response is received, the operator then activates the Stinger system: the battery powers the gyro and electronics, and the coolant chills the seeker to produce the greatest possible temperature differential. On receiving an aural system that the Stinger's seeker has locked onto the target, the operator uses his trigger to fire the missile. The booster stage pops the missile out of the launcher tube, and the sustainer ignites only when the missile has coasted far enough ahead of the operator to avoid any possibility of the sustainer burning him. Thereafter the engagement is automatic, the missile's guidance electronics using proportional navigation laws to home on the target, special circuitry modifying the steering command to make the missile hit the aircraft rather than its exhaust plume. The operator discards the spent container and fits a fresh round.

The Stinger was first test-fired in 1974. Early trials confirmed that the missile possessed the required performance, but that the seeker unit left much to be required in accuracy and reliability. Initial attempts to rectify these limitations were generally unsuccessful, a fact highlighted by the US Army's urgent contract with Ford Aerospace for an Alternate Stinger with laser beam-riding guidance: the laser was built into the launcher unit, requiring the operator to keep his sight on the target until the missile impacted.

In August 1976 an Alternate Stinger successfully engaged a supersonic target, but by this time progress was finally being made with the IR Stinger, allowing production to begin in the late 1970s. The weapon was finally introduced in 1981 as the FIM-92A Stinger, and has proved generally successful. The missile and launcher weigh 30lb (13.6kg), or 33.3lb (15.1kg) with the IFF system and battery. The early problems have been fully overcome, and the Stinger has been widely accepted.

Experience soon showed, however, that the Stinger has the same vulnerability as the Redeye to IR countermeasures (IRCM). This led to the development from 1977 of the more advanced FIM-92B Stinger-POST, which is currently in production, and features a passive optical scanning technique (POST) seeker with cells sensitive to UV as well as IR radiation: this image-scan optical processing system (in place of the Stinger's reticle and discrete components) uses a microprocessor to compare the two types of return and thus provides better discrimination between the target and decoys, and also between the target and the ground in low-altitude engagements. The basic shoulder-launched Stinger provides the USA and its allies with a capable man-portable SAM whose main tactical limitations are both to deal with targets at medium altitudes and an inability to engage targets flying lower than the launcher. The latter translates into the impossibility of hilltop Stinger positions to fire down onto fixed- and rotary-wing warplanes operating in valleys.

One of the most important land-mobile SAMs yet to have appeared, the BAe Rapier was conceived in the early 1960s as a point-defence weapon to provide battlefield formations with the capability of destroying all types of attack warplanes (in the performance bracket from hovering helicopters to terrain-following supersonic fixed-wing machines) at ranges greater than those of the attackers' stand-off weapons. The origins of the programme lay with an army requirement for a point-defence missile, originally to have been the PT428. By 1962 it was clear that this would be too expensive a

system, however, so the army decided to adopt the Mauler being developed for the US Army by the Pomona Division of Convair. However, this system was plagued by development problems and would also be very expensive, so in 1963 the army decided once more on a British system.

The Guided Weapons Division of the British Aircraft Corporation (later British Aerospace Dynamics Group and now the British Aerospace Army Weapons Division) had been working on a private-venture system called Sightline since 1961, and this formed the basis for the ET316 proposal of September 1964. The resultant development programme was a model of its kind, and key features of the missile were supersonic performance combined with great accuracy: the former was designed to maximise the missile's kinetic energy and reduce the time available for the target to implement any sort of countermeasures, and the latter to make possible the carriage of a very small warhead. This is of the semi-armour-piercing type that achieves its destructive effect by actual penetration of the target before detonation in the confined and vulnerable spaces inside the target structure.

Although severe doubts were expressed in some quarters about the tactical utility of a weapon with so small a warhead containing only 1.1lb (0.5kg) of explosive, the Rapier's warhead has proved more than adequate in service. Indeed, so great is the missile's accuracy that the general term 'hittile' was coined for the Rapier: the degree of accuracy is attested by the fact that in one test firing the missile pierced a towed target only 7.5in (0.19m) in diameter. Another advantage is the elimination of a costly proximity fuse, allowing the missile to be used against very-low-level targets without fear of the premature detonation that can be induced in proximity fuses by ground returns. This latter capability has been proved by test firings against ground targets to meet US Army requirements: an Alvis Saracen armoured personnel carrier was hit in the turret, the following explosion blew off the turret and otherwise devastated the vehicle.

Thus the BAC decision was for a smaller, lighter and cheaper weapon than the contemporary generation of larger missiles possessing comparable performance, and this has been a useful asset in the Rapier's undoubted commercial success. Test firings began in 1965 (the year in which the US Mauler system was cancelled) and were almost universally successful. Production contracts for the British army and RAF Regiment were issued in 1968, and the Rapier Mk 1 entered service in 1971 for an initial operational capability in 1973. Since that time the missile has been built in large numbers and has been integrated into a number of increasingly sophisticated overall systems. The Rapier has been blooded in combat, and during the Falklands War of 1982 was credited with the confirmed destruction of 14 Argentine warplanes and with the probable destruction of another six. The Rapier system has demonstrated an average single-shot kill probability of more than 70 per cent, this percentage rising markedly in salvo engagements of a single target.

In configuration the Rapier adheres to the basic design philosophy of BAe surface-launched missiles: the body is cylindrical (with a slim tapered nose) and carries on the mid-body section a cruciform of low-aspect-ratio delta wings and at the tail a cruciform of high-aspect-ratio control fins, which are indexed in line with the wings and activated by powerful gas generators for rapid and accurate control response at low level: throughout its life the Rapier has provided constant proof of its agility to pull high-g turns at all ranges against manoeuvring and fast-crossing targets.

The basic Rapier system introduced in 1971 is the Towed Rapier, and this comprises the four-round launcher plus surveillance radar and associated Cossor IFF subsystem on a two-wheel trailer for towing by any light cross-

Successor to the Redeye, the FIM-92 Stinger is an altogether more capable surface-to-air missile of the man-portable type, and included in its capabilities are the ability to engage oncoming aircraft. This gives the infantryman a chance to destroy an attacking warplane before it had dropped its weapons.

country vehicle such as a Land Rover, the Barr & Stroud optical tracker, a secondary sight, a tactical control unit and a generator (all carried by the towing vehicle), and nine reload missiles carried in a second vehicle. The towing vehicle carries the basic crew of two, while the second vehicle accommodates three personnel. It requires three people to deploy the Towed Rapier system (a task taking about 15 minutes and requiring the interconnection by cable of the various components spread out within a circle with a diameter of 100ft/30.5m) and two people to reload missiles. Although one person can then operate the system in simple conditions, it is more common for the operator to be supported by a tactical controller when there is a mix of friendly and hostile warplanes in the area, or in conditions of severe ECM. Once in position, the Rapier fire unit (launcher) is levelled on four jacks and its wheels are removed, while the operator sets the parameters of the 'taboo' facility which prevents the firing of a missile on bearings and elevations obstructed by physical items such as buildings, hills or woods. The operator can also use an engagement zone selector to create closed arcs of fire: warplanes appearing in any of these arcs are signalled by a visual signal rather than the standard aural warning, and while no target can be engaged in such a preselected closed arc, a target engaged outside such an arc can be followed into it by an intercepting missile. The four ready-use missiles carried on the fire unit's towing vehicle are removed from their containers, in which they are treated as no-maintenance rounds of ammunition, and loaded onto the launcher's four rails, which can be elevated through an arc of 65 degrees (between –5 degrees and +60 degrees) and are disposed as a vertical pair on each side of the central pedestal, which can be traversed through 360 degrees.

Once the system is in position and the missiles have been loaded onto their rails, the Racal-Decca surveillance radar is switched on. This is mounted in the large cylindrical pedestal of the fire unit, and its antenna completes one turn every second, ensuring surveillance through 360 degrees out to a range of 13,000yds (11,885m). The radar is a coherent pulse-Doppler equipment and can detect warplanes between ground level and 10,000ft (3,050m). If a possible target is detected, the system automatically IFFs it before alerting the operator: if the echo proves to be friendly, the preliminary data are wiped out and the radar goes back to its search; but if the echo proves to be hostile, the radar and fire unit's onboard computer begin the solution of the resultant fire-control problem while alerting the operator with an aural signal and slewing the launcher and the operator's optical tracker to the correct bearing. The operator then acquires and tracks the target using a small control column, whose movements are outputted from the tracker to the fire unit. The operator is automatically informed when the target is

Opposite: One of the most important and effective tactical surface-to-air missiles currently in service, and a weapon that is still under active development, the Rapier is a short-range weapon with nearly unjammable guidance and very considerable accuracy. The type is used in conjunction with a number of towed and self-propelled launchers.

Following page: Altogether larger and longer-ranged than the Rapier, the MIM-104 Patriot is an advanced surface-to-air missile used in conjunction with an advanced radar and fire-control system to provide an all-altitude capability against aircraft and, under a growing number circumstances, surface-to-surface ballistic missiles.

within the system's launch parameters, and then fires a missile. The reaction time can be as little as six seconds from target detection to missile launch, which offers very useful advantages in the engagement of fast-moving targets that may pop up from behind masking terrain quite close to their intended targets. After launch the missile is rapidly gathered, the fire unit having been aligned automatically so that the missile flies into the tracker's line of sight immediately after launch. The operator uses his joystick control to keep the tracker's binocular sight fixed firmly on the target, and a TV missile tracker boresighted to the optical tracker watches the flares on the missile's tail: any angular deviations are measured, and the system's computer automatically generates the signals necessary to bring the missile back into the centre of the tracker's line of sight, and to keep it there until impact with the target. These control signals are transmitted to the missile via a Racal-Decca microwave link whose antenna is mounted on the front of the cylindrical housing for the surveillance radar.

Reaction time for a second launch against the same target, or for another target within the operator's field of vision, can be as short as three seconds after the impact of the first missile, and when all four missiles have been expended, the two-man reload crew can load another four missiles on the fire unit's rails in 2½ minutes. Its overall capabilities combine with its rapid reloading facility to give the Towed Rapier system considerable tactical importance.

Another useful feature of the Towed Rapier has been its basic design on a modular basis, and this has proved particularly advantageous in the updating of the system. Since the type entered service, such updates have been undertaken on a constant basis to keep the weapon fully abreast of developments. From the beginning of the Towed Rapier's service life, reliability in the order of 90 per cent has been the norm, and this figure has been improved usefully by the introduction of built-In test equipment and a degree of redundancy. Apart from improving reliability, these two features have a beneficial battlefield function in improving survivability and speeding the repair process for damaged equipments.

The Rapier system has also been installed in a tracked chassis for improved operational compatibility with mobile forces, and has been considerably upgraded in the basic missile as well as in the system's ancillary systems.

The Raytheon MIM-104 Patriot is a highly capable air-defence weapon designed to supplement the Raytheon MIM-23B Improved HAWK and to replace the Western Electric MIM-14B/C Nike Hercules missiles in the medium-range roles. It had become clear to the US Army as early as 1960 that the combination of the scarcely-mobile Nike Hercules and cumbersome HAWK systems would be inadequate to provide US Army combat formations with any real measure of area air-defence capability in the type of mobile warfare anticipated for the 1970s and later. From 1961, therefore, the service instituted a feasibility study under the designation FABMDS (Field Army Ballistic Missile Defence System), and this led to the AADS-70 (Army Air Defense System for the 1970s) requirement.

The basic design parameters had been settled by 1965, and the US Army Missile Command then began to undertake the hardware validation phase of the weapon, at that time designated SAM-D. By August of the same year the requirement for the missile had been finalised, calling for capability under the most adverse weather, geographic, climatic and electronic conditions against warplane targets at all altitudes, and also against SRBMs. The service's request for proposals was issued in April 1966 and elicited responses from Hughes, Raytheon and RCA, and in May 1967 Raytheon received contractual authorisation to proceed as prime contractor for the SAM-D programme. The main subcontractors were Hazeltine (IFF system), Martin Marietta (missile airframe and launcher) and Thiokol (rocket motor).

The original concept had envisaged the complete system embarked on just two M548 tracked carriers (one with the missile launcher and the other with the radar) for a high degree of battlefield mobility, but by the second half of the 1970s this had declined to a firing battery of three truck units and eight truck-towed launcher stations: the basic firing unit had thus not only increased in overall size, but had declined in mobility. It can be argued, however, that the capabilities of the Patriot system are so great that it need not keep up with the forward elements involved in a mobile campaign. For tactical operations, four or six batteries constitute a Patriot battalion, which therefore has 32 or 48 Patriot launchers as the standard battery; eight firing trailers together with the associated MPQ-53 multi-function radar. The battalion therefore has a theoretical maximum complement of 128 or 192 Patriot missiles excluding reloads, which are allocated at the rate of six per M901 firing trailer.

The missile was first test-fired in 1970 with fully guided test firings following in 1975, and is superficially an unremarkable vehicle in aerodynamic and structural terms. The body is a comparatively wide-diameter cylinder with an ogival nosecone and a rear-mounted cruciform of modestly swept control fins. Under the nosecone is the antenna for the command mid-course and semi-active radar terminal guidance systems, trailed by the control electronics, the warhead and associated fuse system, the advanced rocket motor of which no details have been released, and the high-powered actuator system for the fins, which are claimed to give this body-lift missile a degree of agility unmatched by any manned warplane.

The missile is delivered as a complete round inside a sealed transportation container that doubles as the launcher. The sealed-in missile is certified for a shelf life of five years, and a special vehicle is used to fit the four containers onto the M901 launcher. This is carried on an M860 two-axle semi-trailer towed by a 5-ton M818 6x6 tractor. The M860 is disconnected from its tractor and then levelled on four jacks before the beginning of an engagement, and has its own 20 hp (14.91kW) diesel generator for electrical power. The missile containers fit into a special frame that is traversed and elevated under command of the battery's fire-control system, the orders being relayed by secure radio data-link. The M901 launcher can be traversed through 360 degrees, but is locked in position before an engagement as the launcher does not follow the target. The firing trailer has its missile canisters at the fixed launch elevation angle of +30 degrees.

Normally four or five (but up to eight) launchers are controlled from the MSQ-104 Engagement Control Centre (ECC), giving a total of between 16 and 32 missiles (excluding reloads) per battery. Apart from the launcher reload vehicle, this is the only manned equipment in the battery, is carried in a 5.6-ton shelter on the back of an M814 6x6 truck, and accommodates the system's two operators, the digital weapon-control computer and two tactical display consoles, with power provided by the associated MQJ-20 6x6 powerplant truck, which supplies both the ECC and MPQ-53 radar from two 200hp (149kW) turbine-driven generators. The ECC's 24-bit high-speed digital computer is extremely capable, and is a software-controlled unit with twin (optionally triple) computer/memory subunits fully capable of exercising tactical control over a whole interception sequence from radar scheduling to intercept assessment via weapon assignment, missile launch, hardware monitoring and the full spectrum of fault detection, location and

isolation. The computer provides the essential man/machine interfaces via the tactical display consoles.

The system allows several operating modes, ranging from fully automatic down to computer-aided manual interceptions, and fire-control data are supplied automatically to the relevant launcher unit via the battery's secure data-link network. The advanced software developed for the ECC's computer falls into three main groups: operational readiness, real-time control of the fire unit, and fault detection analysis. The first group brings the complete outfit to a state of readiness by loading all appropriate data into the fire-control computer and radar computers, and by the collection and storage of firing position data (antenna orientation, radar coverage limitations, blind spots and horizon contours). The second group includes functions such as control of the radar (in search, target tracking, IFF interrogation, missile acquisition and tracking, and transmission of missile-guidance commands in the mid-course and terminal phases of the flight); selection and processing of information for the operators, and implementation of operator commands; selection of missile launcher, and transmission of the appropriate laying and launch commands; communication via digital data-link with higher-level command sources as well as neighbouring Patriot batteries; and monitoring of battery status. This programme group also carries out threat evaluation and threat prioritisation, allowing anything from fully automatic to manual engagement depending on the engagement mode in operation.

The real core of the system, however, is the Raytheon MPQ-53 radar, and the significance of this equipment is attested by the fact that its manufacturer was selected as prime contractor in preference to the missile maker. Whereas the Nike Hercules and HAWK systems require four separate radar types (some of them in multiples so that one equipment can be allocated to each launcher), the Patriot system has only a single radar. This multi-function equipment provides the whole battery with surveillance, target acquisition, tracking, ranging and range rate, as well as missile tracking, command guidance and target illumination facilities: this is made possible by the advanced nature of the complete equipment, which uses computer control for the enormously complex time-sharing system that makes the system operate effectively. The radar operates with its planar antenna locked at an angle of +67.5 degrees to the horizontal. Like the launcher, the radar is installed on an M860 two-axle semi-trailer, which is unhitched from its tractor and levelled with jacks before being brought into operation. The primary elements are a shelter accommodating the bulk of the equipment's electronics, and a large planar antenna unit accommodating the separate phased-array elements for target acquisition and tracking, and missile tracking (5,161 elements in the main 8ft/2.44m main antenna). The array is also the location for the supplementary arrays associated with track-via-missile system (251 elements), and with the Hazeltine TPX-46(V)7 IFF system.

The programme was characterised by a number of innovative technologies that inevitably caused delays before they could be brought to fruition. The programme also proved considerably more expensive than first envisaged, and this resulted in the US Army's decision to stretch out the development phase as a means of reducing yearly research and development costs. In the event, full-scale engineering development did not begin until 1972, and in 1974 the stretch in the development phase was used to validate the system's unique track-via-missile (TVM) guidance method: even as the radar tracks the target and missile, the missile's own two-way data link provides the fire-control computer with up-to-the-second data about

139

the missile's position and performance, optimising the computer's ability to shape the Patriot's trajectory for maximum range and accuracy before the activation of the missile's semi-active terminal guidance. In 1975 a series of 14 test firings yielded 12 complete successes and one partial success, resulting in a 1976 decision to press ahead with development at an accelerated rate. Further delay resulted from the 1977 decision to replace the missile's onboard analogue computer system with a new digital unit, but this delay was vindicated in 1984 by four successes in four test launches against targets operating with assorted ECM.

The Patriot is launched through the frangible cover of its container, the Thiokol rocket motor providing extremely potent acceleration and a very high maximum speed. A large proportion of the missile's weight is attributable to the solid propellants for this motor, the object being to provide high speed over long range as a means of destroying the target beyond the range of its stand-off weapons and of reducing the time available to the target for the implementation of countermeasures. The spent container is removed by the reload vehicle and a fresh round installed on the launcher. The first Patriot units were formed in 1984, and the missile became operational in 1986. Despite the length of its development programme, the Patriot is still at the very forefront of surface-to-air missile technology and capability, due largely to its excellent radar and flight performance.

Raytheon is continuing to develop the system, the prime objects being improved capability against targets using advanced ECM, tactical ballistic missiles, cruise missiles and other targets with low radar signatures. The use of software-controlled computer systems gives the Patriot great flexibility, and in 1986 a Patriot was directed with the aid of special software to the interception of a Vought MGM-52 Lance ballistic missile at a height of 26,000ft (7,925m) some 14,250yds (13,030m) down-range of the Patriot's launch position. The first firing of a Patriot Anti-Tactical Missile was undertaken in 1987, the missile successfully intercepting another Patriot, which was used because its performance and radar signature approximate those of the latest generation of tactical ballistic missiles fielded by the USSR. In 1988 the US Army completed a patriot anti-tactical ballistic missile capability 1 (PAC-1) programme to update the software of operational Patriots and to allow interception of ballistic missiles such as the SS-21 'Scarab' and SS-1 'Scud' battlefield missiles. The programme improved the search-and-track algorithms in the radar computer software to give the Patriot system the ability to intercept an incoming missile and knock it off course, but probably without destroying its warhead.

Further development was concentrated in the short term on the PAC-2 programme for a new warhead/fuse combination together with improved missile guidance algorithms. These provide a higher level of accuracy and lethality, including the ability to intercept an incoming missile at speeds between Mach 6 and Mach 8 with sufficient accuracy to destroy the missile's warhead section.

All Patriots delivered since 1989 have been of the PAC-2 type, and the basic anti-missile capabilities of the Patriot for the interception of short-range ballistic missiles were confirmed in the 1991 Gulf War. During this campaign, Patriot missiles successfully intercepted a number of 'Scud' missiles fired by the Iraqis at targets in Israel and Saudi Arabia, although the Patriot's lack of ceiling and a devastating warhead meant that large portions of the 'Scud' missiles continued on ballistic trajectories to cause some measure of damage.

Part of the MIM-104 Patriot's capabilities stem from its track-via-missile system, in which target data from the missile's active radar terminal guidance package are downloaded to the launcher system and its fire-control computer for the generation of a continuously computed intercept course whose details are data-linked to the missile as a means of shaping the trajectory, and therefore securing the double objectives of maximising range and securing an interception as far distant as possible from the warplane's objective.

Glossary

ACTIVE HOMING type of homing based on the use of an on-board target detection system using an emitter

BATTERY group of four or six guns (with command post, communications etc) calibrated to fire as a single weapon

BEAM RIDING GUIDANCE type of guidance in which the weapon rides along the path of a beam (radar or laser) extending to the target from the launcher or other designation site

BOMB type of shell fired by a mortar

BOMBLET type of submunition carried by a shell or missile for the creation of a scattering effect

BREECH rear end of barrel into which the propellant and projectile are loaded, now universally by an opening breech mechanism providing direct access to this section of the weapon

CALIBRE diameter of bore, and also used to express the length of the barrel in terms of L/x where the Length is expressed in multiples of the calibre (L/45, for example, describes a barrel 45 times the length of its calibre)

CARRIAGE the wheels, axle(s), trail(s), recoil gear etc on which the barrel is mounted

CARTRIDGE made-up charge(s) of propellant containing in bags or in a fixed metal cartridge case attached to the rear of the projectile

CEP the Circular Error Probable is the measure of accuracy of any weapon, and is the radius of the circle into which 50% of the weapons fired are statistically likely to land

COMMAND GUIDANCE type of guidance in which the missile is guided to the moment of impact by commands generated manually, semi-automatically or automatically at the launcher

DETACHMENT crew of a gun

DIRECT FIRE the type of artillery fire in which the target is visible from the gun position

DISCARDING SABOT phrase used for the type of very high velocity projectile that is fired from a barrel of greater calibre than the projectile itself, the greater cross section of the barrel permitting increased propulsive affect to be applied to the projectile, which it blocked out to the calibre of the barrel by sabots that drop away as the projectile emerges from the muzzle

ELEVATION angular movement of barrel in the vertical plane to vary trajectory and thus range

EQUIPMENT word used for the whole of an artillery piece including the gun, carriage, sights, stores etc

FIXED AMMUNITION type of ammunition in which the projectile is attached at the front of a metal case containing the propellant to speed the loading of quick-firing guns

FRAGMENTATION the breaking up of the wall of a shell to provide fragments or splinters travelling outward from the point of detonation and lethal velocity

FUSE device fitted to a shell or other explosive device to initiate the detonation of the explosive filling at the desired moment (before impact, on impact or after impact)

GUN higher-velocity weapon firing its projectile with a relatively flat trajectory

HEAT HE Anti-Tank warhead of the hollow-charge principle

HESH HE Squash Head warhead designed to spread on impact before detonation, when a sock wave is sent through the target armour to blow off lethal fragments of plate from the inside of the armour

HOLLOW CHARGE warhead with a charge of explosive round a shaped liner, the detonation resulting in a stream of vapourised gas and metal that strikes the target armour at very high velocity and extremely high temperature to burn a hole through it

HOWITZER lower-velocity weapon firing its projectile with a relatively high trajectory to plunge onto the target

INDIRECT FIRE the type of artillery fire in which the target is not visible from the gun position

INERTIAL GUIDANCE type of computer-based guidance based on accelerometers to detect any deviations from the planned trajectory

MORTAR piece of ordnance usually mounted on a baseplate and based on a smooth-bore barrel, and generally using muzzle-loaded ammunition for high-angle fire

MUZZLE BRAKE device used to trap propellant gases in front of the muzzle to reduce recoil

OPTRONIC HOMING type of homing based on the use of an image of the target locked into the guidance package and sought in the view provided by the weapon's TV or imaging infra-red sensor

PASSIVE HOMING type of homing based on the use of an on-board target detection system not using an emitter

SEMI-ACTIVE HOMING type of homing based on the use of an on-board target detection system of the passive type to home on the energy of an active emitter and then reflected by the target

TRAIL long member by which the gun carriage is towed and, in firing position, in lowered to the ground to improve the weapon's stability

TRAVERSE angular movement of the barrel or complete piece of artillery in the horizontal plane

Index